SEA DEFENCE WORKS

> . . . *I have seen the hungry ocean gain*
> *Advantage on the Kingdom of the shore,*
> *And the firm soil win of the watery main,*
> *Increasing store with loss, and loss with store.*
> Wm. Shakespeare, Sonnet LXIV

SEA DEFENCE WORKS

Design, Construction and Emergency Works

Roland Berkeley Thorn
B.Sc., C.Eng., F.I.C.E., F.I.W.E., M.I. Struct.E.,
Chief Design and Planning Engineer, Kent River Authority

and

J. C. F. Simmons
C.Eng., M.I.C.E., M.I.W.E.,
Senior Assistant Design Engineer, Kent River Authority

LONDON
BUTTERWORTHS

THE BUTTERWORTH GROUP

ENGLAND Butterworth & Co (Publishers) Ltd
London: 88 Kingsway, WC2B 6AB

AUSTRALIA Butterworth & Co (Australia) Ltd
Sydney: 586 Pacific Highway Chatswood, NSW 2067
Melbourne: 343 Little Collins Street, 3000
Brisbane: 240 Queen Street, 4000

CANADA Butterworth & Co (Canada) Ltd
Toronto: 14 Curity Avenue, 374

NEW ZEALAND Butterworth & Co (New Zealand) Ltd
Wellington: 26–28 Waring Taylor Street, 1
Auckland: 35 High Street, 1

SOUTH AFRICA Butterworth & Co (South Africa) (Pty) Ltd
Durban, 152–154 Gale Street

Formerly published under the title,
The Design of Sea Defence Works, 1960
Second Edition, *Sea Defence Works*, 1971

ISBN 0 408 70201 X

*Filmset by Filmtype Services Limited,
Scarborough
Printed in England by The Whitefriars Press Ltd,
London and Tonbridge*

Preface

The seaborne landings of the 1939–45 war gave a stimulus to the science of coastal hydraulics, particularly in America, and once started, the momentum continued after the war. In Britain, R. C. H. Russell at the newly-founded Hydraulics Research Station carried on work in this field in the steps of the great pioneer, R. A. Bagnold of Imperial College, London, and after 1953 research was further encouraged in Britain by the setting up of the Advisory Committee on Sea Defence Research.

Towards the end of the nineteen fifties it seemed to me that the healthy progress in coastal hydraulics was not matched by the publication of suitable textbooks on the design of sea defence works. I felt that a book on this subject was needed, based soundly on experience and upon the principles and findings of this rapidly developing branch of hydraulics. That was the purpose of my book *The Design of Sea Defence Works,* published in 1960.

A decade has passed, and from the success of that book it would seem that a great number of my fellow engineers practising in coastal engineering agree that that was the right approach.

My colleague, J. C. F. Simmons, and I have critically examined the text of the book and have revised, up-dated, expanded and metricated it for this new edition. Because its scope covers not only design but also construction and emergency works we have named it *Sea Defence Works.*

The book deals with sea defence practice in the United Kingdom, where the construction and maintenance of sea defences is under the jurisdiction of coast protection authorities and river authorities. Coast protection authorities derive their powers from the Coast Protection Act 1949 and are concerned with the prevention of erosion of lengths of coast above highest sea level, whereas the river authorities' powers are derived from the Land Drainage Acts of 1930 and 1961 and are concerned with the defence of low-lying coasts against tidal flooding.

R.B.T.

Little Rede,
Banky Meadow,
Barming,
Kent.
1971

Acknowledgments

For permission to reproduce the following the authors' thanks are due to:

J. I. Taylor, M.B.E., B.Sc., C.Eng., F.I.C.E., F.I.W.E., Chief Engineer, Kent River Authority—Photographs and diagrams of Kent River Authority Sea Defence Works.

Thorndike Saville, Jnr. U.S. Army Coastal Engineering Research Center, Corps of Engineers, Council on Wave Research—Paper reproduced (from the *Proceedings of the Sixth International Conference on Coastal Engineering, 1957,* University of Florida, published by the U.S. Council on Wave Research, University of California) in the Appendix to Chapter 1, Wave Run-up on Composite Slopes.

Société d'Exploitation de Brevets pour Travaux à la Mer (Sotramer)— Photograph of the Marine Drive Sea Wall, Bombay.

C. E. Tiffen—Photographs of the Northern Sea Wall under construction.

J. Evans, B.Sc., C.Eng., F.I.C.E., Consulting Engineer—Photograph of the Pett Sea Wall.

Mobbs and English, Consulting Engineers—Photographs of permeable revetments and groynes on the Norfolk and Hampshire coasts.

Ministerie van Verkeer en Waterstaat, The Hague, Holland—Photographs of the closure of the Schelphoek breach.

H.M.S.O. and Hydraulics Research Station, Wallingford—Photographs of the Sheerness Sea Wall model.

Contents

Contents

3 SEA WALLS, ESTUARY WALLS AND COUNTERWALLS

Soil Mechanics Considerations

General Considerations

Wall Materials and Construction

4 THE HYDRAULIC DESIGN OF SEA WALL PROFILES, AND REVETMENT DETAILS

Contents

Contents

Introduction to the First Edition

In *The Design of Land Drainage Works* (Butterworths, 1959) I commented that the design of Sea Defence Works lacked largely a satisfactory theoretical basis. For, until comparatively recently, design in this branch of engineering had proceeded by trial-and-error methods, and that is why most of the books that have been written on the subject leave the reader in bewilderment, since they give detailed accounts of the structural design of various sea walls (many archaic) around the coasts of Britain but often omit clear descriptions of the conditions prevailing at the sites and explanations and comments on the suitability and adequacy of the chosen designs.

Of any sea wall two questions have to be asked; firstly, is the design hydraulically satisfactory, and secondly, is it structurally satisfactory? Frequently it will be found that where experience of many years shows an existing sea defence work to be adequate the present design is one that has evolved from past unsatisfactory defences.

Coastal conditions seldom attain complete year-to-year stability and we are often faced with the problem of a deteriorating foreshore. The maintenance and strengthening of natural sea defences are the first aims of the sea defence engineer. Indeed, unless the foreshore can be (or becomes) stabilised by one means or another there is no end to the additional works required on a sea wall as the foreshore drops, exposing the toe, and as the greater depths of water in front of the wall allow bigger waves to break with greater impact on it.

We cannot afford costly failures, and trial and error must be reduced to a minimum. To achieve this we must endeavour to understand the basic factors affecting the foreshore conditions, and must try to design from our accumulated knowledge of these factors sea defences that will fulfil our requirements with the minimum expenditure. Much detailed research is at present being carried out that is giving us a clearer picture of our problems, much has still to be learned, and the wise engineer will rarely be found dogmatic on any aspect of sea defence.

Introduction

No man can have a completely comprehensive knowledge of any subject, yet it is remarkable how infrequently authors frankly tell their readers of their own limitations. This book is based on the author's experience of the design and construction of many millions of pounds' worth of works carried out on over 150 miles of sea defences maintained by the Kent River Board. These defences range from sand dunes to earthen estuary walls and from timber groynes to huge structures such as the Northern Sea Wall from Reculver to Birchington, which is one of the most massive sea walls in the United Kingdom. The wide variation in foreshore conditions and many different problems encountered have given the author a good insight into the subject of sea defences and at the same time have left him a humbler man in consequence, for, in the words of à Kempis, 'Be not therefore extolled in thine own mind for any art or science, but rather let the knowledge given thee, make thee more humble and cautious'.

Full acknowledgment must be made of the debt owed to Mr. J. I. Taylor, M.B.E., B.Sc., M.I.C.E., M.I.W.E., Chief Engineer to the Kent River Board, whose clarity of mind and profound knowledge of foreshore phenomena have greatly influenced and guided the author in formulating his ideas on this most contentious subject.

R.B.T.

Maidstone, March, 1960

Chapter 1

Tides and Waves

1.1 TIDES GENERALLY

From the earliest times, in Europe, the relation has been realised between the tides and the phases of the moon. It was known that the highest high water levels and the greatest difference in levels between high and low water (spring tides) occurred about two days after the times of full or new moon, approximately every 15 days, and that the lowest high water levels and the least difference in levels between high and low water (neap tides) also occurred every 15 days near the times of half moon at the first and last quarters.

1.2 TIDE TABLES

The sea defence engineer is mainly concerned with the results of tidal research and only very indirectly with the mathematical theory. A great deal of this practical information will be found in the *Admiralty Tide Tables*. The information given is as follows:

(a) Times and levels of high and low water on any day at Standard and Secondary Ports round the coast.
(b) Mean high and low water spring tides, mean high and low water neap tides, mean tide level, at ports round the coast.
(c) Height of the tide at a given time, and time at which the tide reaches a given height at ports round the coast.

The information is based on the assumption that the rise and fall of the tide conform to simple cosine curves. Special tables are given for determining the values for localities where shallow water effects are considerable.

1.3 EFFECT ON TIDE LEVELS OF BAROMETRIC PRESSURE AND WIND

A change of one inch in the height of the barometer causes a change of about one foot in sea level. Sea levels are raised by winds in the directions towards which the winds are blowing and conversely are lowered in the directions from which the winds are coming. The converging or diverging of coastlines increases or decreases these variations in sea levels. For example, water driven into or out of the more confined area of the southern part of the North Sea by northerly or southerly gales considerably affects sea levels in the Thames Estuary, producing material variations from the predicted tide levels. In the open sea, however, winds alone would not generally alter the level by more than about 0·3 metre.

1.4 TIDAL STREAMS

With the flow and ebb of the tide are associated tidal streams along the coast. In shallow channels the tidal curve can become distorted, the rise becoming more rapid than the fall; under these conditions the tidal current is greater on the flood tide than on the ebb tide in the opposite direction. All along the coast the inshore current need not necessarily be in the same direction as the off-shore tidal stream; for example, the effect of a headland may be to cause an eddy giving an inshore current locally in the opposite direction to the tidal stream. Information with regard to the directions and velocities of tidal streams at definite points and at tabulated periods in hours before and after high water at a nearby Port may be obtained from the relevant Admiralty Charts.

1.5 SURGES AND SEICHES

Large increases in sea level caused by the meteorological conditions described in section 1.3 and of speed similar to that of the tidal wave are known as storm surges. *Figure 1* shows the tide levels recorded on 31 Jan./1 Feb. 1953 at Southend, and the surge that was superimposed on the tide. High water was nearly 2·5 m above the predicted level.

Seiches are also non-tidal fluctuations in sea level but of short period oscillation compared with tidal waves, and are caused by sudden meteorological conditions such as the passage of a line squall. The seiche that occurred on 3 July 1946 on the south coast of England caused sea level to drop 1·25 m in a few minutes and then to rise rapidly 2·5 m.

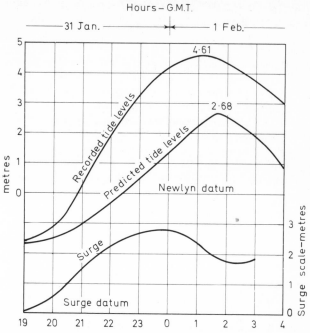

*Figure 1. Tide level curve at Southend on 31 Jan./1 Feb. 1953
(based on Port of London Authority data)*

1.6 WAVES

When ideal waves move over deep water all water particles move in vertical circles, the diameter of the circles described by the surface particles being equal to the wave height (*H*), that is the height in metres from crest to trough, and the diameters decreasing with depth. The movement decreases rapidly with depth and below a depth of one wavelength the movement is less than 1/500 of the wave height. In shallow water, that is when the depth is equal to or less than half the wave length (from crest to crest), the water particle orbits become ellipses with their major axes horizontal. For intermediate depths the orbits are circular towards the surface and elliptical towards the bottom. With increasing depth the vertical motion diminishes more rapidly than the horizontal motion, so that the deeper the particle the flatter is its orbit.

Wind-generated waves, except in the form of ocean swell on calm water, cannot strictly be termed ideal, although for practical purposes they may be regarded as behaving very similarly. The characteristic shape of wind-driven waves is a steeper slope on the leeward side of the crest and a gentler slope on the windward side.

1.7 MASS TRANSPORT AND RIP CURRENTS

The forward movement of the water particles, as a whole is not in fact entirely compensated by the backward movement and as a result there is a general movement of the water in the direction of travel of the waves—this is known as mass transport. When waves reach the coast, therefore, the sea level rises and there is flow from regions of high waves to regions of low waves, and to sea. Narrow bands of water moving away from the shore are called rip currents and constitute a means whereby water brought to the coast by mass transport returns to sea.

1.8 WAVE PERIOD, LENGTH, VELOCITY AND REFRACTION

The wave period (P) is the time in seconds between the passing of two adjacent crests past a stationary point. The wave length (L) is the distance in metres between two adjacent crests, and if V is the velocity in metres per second of the wave, $L = PV$. In the English Channel the wave period does not usually exceed 6 sec, and for the common run of waves in the Atlantic it is from 6 to 8 sec.

Airy's expression, in metric units, for the velocity of waves is:

$$V = \sqrt{\frac{gL}{2\pi} \tanh \frac{2\pi D}{L}}$$

where D is the still water depth in metres. When D becomes greater than L, tanh $2\pi D/L$ becomes equal to unity, so that in deep water

$$V = \sqrt{\frac{gL}{2\pi}} = 1 \cdot 25 \sqrt{L}$$

When the depth becomes less than one-tenth of the wave length tanh $2\pi D/L$ approaches $2\pi D/L$ and V then equals $\sqrt{gD}$, and this is the expression of most use to sea defence engineers. It has been found that generally these expressions can be applied with only a small error to natural wind-generated waves and therefore their use in sea defence design problems is considerable. Wave velocities for various depths may be read directly from Design

Chart A. The expression shows that as waves move into shallow-ing water the velocity of the waves nearest the shore reduces and the wave length therefore decreases.

Another effect of this reduction in velocity is that as waves approach a shore obliquely the portions of the waves nearest the shore slow down so that the waves as a whole swing round and tend to become parallel to the shore—this is called refraction. In refraction as in reflection sea waves behave similarly to light waves; it is thus possible, by constructing one or more raised areas on the sea bed, to deviate waves passing over them so that calm water occurs at harbour entrances whilst on either side of the entrances heavy wave action continues. An interesting account setting out possible applications of such works has been given by Costa and Perestrelo. Refraction may have a divergent or convergent effect on the waves, in which case the wave heights are correspondingly decreased or increased.

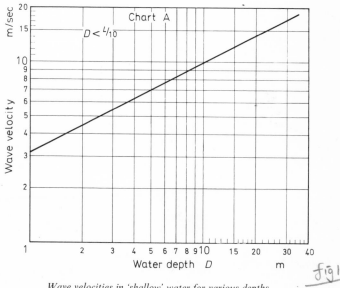

Wave velocities in 'shallow' water for various depths

It is important to note that although direction, velocity and wave length of the waves change as they approach the coast, the wave period remains constant.

When the depth of water becomes less than half the wave length not only do the velocity and length of the waves decrease but the height also alters, at first decreasing slightly and then increasing

(a)

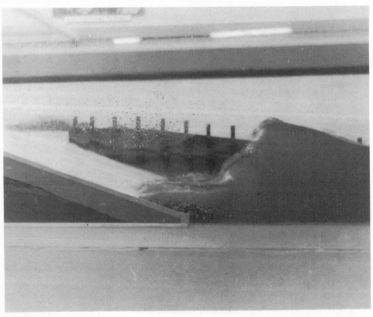

(b)

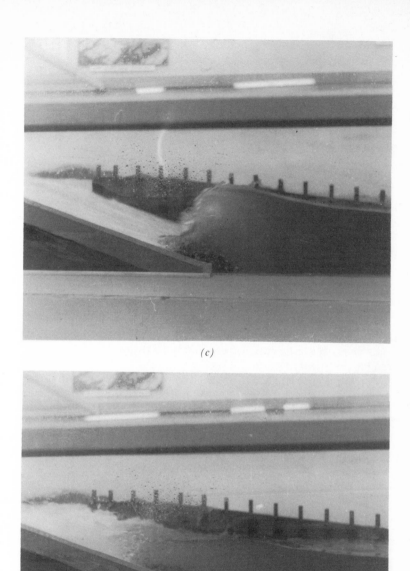

(c)

(d)

Figure 2(a)–(d). Wave breaking on a sloping sea wall apron

to breaking height (for the relevant expressions see Appendix to Chapter 1, pp. 17–26). As the bed rises the wave breaks when the depth of the water below tide level is very approximately equal to four-thirds the wave height (see Appendix to Chapter 1); the steeper the wave and the steeper the bed the greater the breaking depth.

Figure 2(a)–(d) shows the way a wave breaks on a sloping sea wall apron.

1.9 WAVE HEIGHT AND FETCH

In 1874 Thomas Stevenson put forward a formula which, in metric units, gives wave height in metres generated by gales: $H = 0.336\sqrt{F}$; ($0.336\sqrt{F} + 0.762 - 0.261\sqrt[4]{F}$ for fetches under 37 km), where F is the fetch in kilometres.

Although the expression does not take into account the actual wind strength, it has been found reliable in conditions where the wind duration has been sufficiently long. It is based upon (shallow seas) data for the British Isles and may be taken to give the significant wave height, i.e. the average height of the highest one-third of the waves. Wave heights corresponding to various fetches may be read directly from Design Charts B(i) and B(ii).

Another approach, which gives the wave heights and periods to be expected for given fetches and wind speeds, is that of Sverdrup, Munk and Bretschneider, the SMB method, based on deep-water wave data (see Beach Erosion Board publication of 1954 and 'Revisions in Wave Forecasting: Deep and Shallow Water', *Proc. 6th International Conference on Coastal Engineering*). Francis has shown that Stevenson's equations predict about the same wave height as the SMB method if the wind speed is about 40 knots (74 km/h), that is for gale force winds (Beaufort Force 8–9) to which Stevenson intended his expressions to apply. There are also the methods of Suthons and Derbyshire. All these methods are based upon data with very considerable scatter and they can give wide variations in estimates of wave heights. The best advice is to use the expression based upon data derived from conditions which most closely resemble the conditions under consideration.

Fortunately for the sea defence engineer, depth of water seaward of the wall is usually a more important factor than fetch. In the general case it will be found that waves generated by the wind and fetch break and re-form on sub-aqueous sandbanks or in the shallow water in front of the wall, so that the height of the waves that break on the wall is determined by the depths of water seaward of the wall, for the waves break when the depth of water below tide level is very approximately equal to four-thirds the wave height (the relevant expressions are given in the Appendix to Chapter 1). Wave heights may also be determined by the methods given in section 1.12.

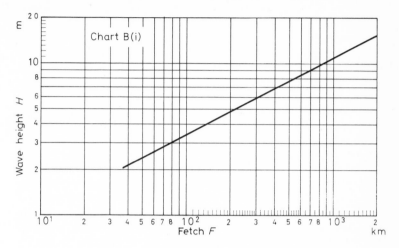

Wave heights corresponding to various fetches over 37 km

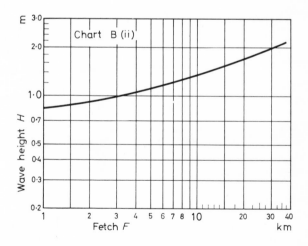

Wave heights corresponding to various fetches under 37 km

1.10 WAVE REFLECTION, CLAPOTIS, AND SWASH

Waves approaching a vertical face (for example, a harbour arm) in sufficiently deep water (depth at least $1 \cdot 5H$), and at an angle are reflected with the angle of incidence equal to the angle of reflection.

Under the same conditions, if the lines of the waves are parallel to the wall the effect of reflection is to form a series of standing waves or clapotis. At fixed distances from the wall exist nodes and anti-nodes; at the nodes there is no movement and at the anti-nodes there is maximum vertical movement from crest to trough. The wall is an anti-nodic position and the movement there from crest to trough is approximately twice the height of the waves out at sea. The effect of oblique incidence is to cause high crests to occur at the intersection of incident and reflected wave crests, and low troughs to occur at the intersection of incident and reflected troughs. A wall slope of 2:1 (horizontal:vertical) is about the steepest for waves to break on it; if the apron is steeper the wave is reflected and does not break.

When a wave breaks on a foreshore or sea wall the uprush of water is called the swash, and the height to which it rises above sea level

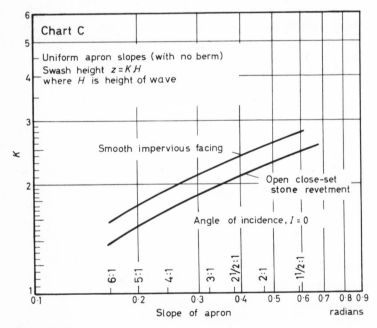

Swash heights for various uniform apron slopes (with no berm)

is known as the swash (or uprush) height, and determines the height of shingle crests (the shingle full) and whether or not sea walls are overtopped. The more impermeable and steep the slope the higher the swash height. From his investigations Bagnold found that the swash height measured vertically from the lowest level of the uncovered beach as the wave breaks was equal to kH, where H was the amplitude of the out-at-sea wave above the same level. For 0·7 cm beach material, k had the value of 1·68, and for 0·3 cm material a value of 1·78.

The formula given below was developed by the Delft Hydraulics Laboratory. Investigations by Wassing have shown that this expression is not as accurate as had been hoped. Whilst academically it should perhaps be discarded, having regard to the complexities of the problem and until a better general expression is forthcoming, for the purpose of approximate preliminary design assessments it is still of use. An obvious defect in the expression is that the wave steepness H/L is not taken into account.

$$ Z = 2.7\, H \sin A \left(\cos I - \frac{B}{L} \right) \sqrt{\frac{\pi}{2A}} $$

where Z is the swash height above mean sea level attained by 2 per cent of the waves, A is the angle in radians of the apron slope, H is the average inshore height of the highest 1/3 of the waves, B is the wall berm width (see section 4.3), I is the angle of incidence of oblique waves, and L is the wave length. The expression is for open, close-set stone revetment, and smooth, impervious facings increase the swash height by about 15 per cent. The swash heights for both classes of revetment may be read directly for various apron slopes from Design Chart C. Chart D for open close-set aprons gives the swash heights for various slopes and berm widths, and Chart E gives similar information for impervious facings. In using the expression, B/L should preferably not be greater than 0·25.

Thorndike Saville has presented an interesting method for determining swash height on composite slopes (including berms) from laboratory-derived curves for single slopes. The method is one of successive approximations and involves replacement of the actual composite slope with a hypothetical single slope obtained from the breaking depth and an estimated run-up value. Comparison of predicted values using this method with model experimental values showed the deviation generally within 10 per cent with a maximum of about 25 per cent. Work by Herbich and Sorensen indicates that the method should preferably be limited to cases where

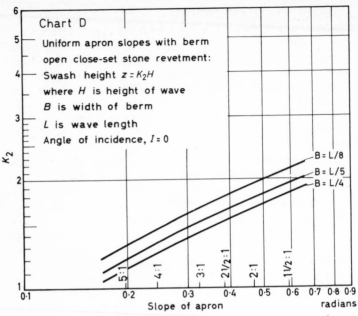

Chart D

Uniform apron slopes with berm
open close-set stone revetment:
Swash height $z = K_2 H$
where H is height of wave
B is width of berm
L is wave length
Angle of incidence, $I = 0$

K_2

B = L/8
B = L/5
B = L/4

5:1 4:1 3:1 2½:1 2:1 1½:1

Slope of apron

radians

Swash heights for various uniform apron slopes and berm widths—open close-set stone revetments

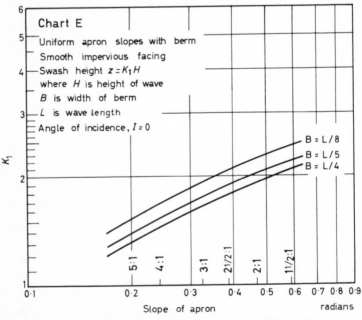

Chart E

Uniform apron slopes with berm
Smooth impervious facing
Swash height $z = K_1 H$
where H is height of wave
B is width of berm
L is wave length
Angle of incidence, $I = 0$

K_1

B = L/8
B = L/5
B = L/4

5:1 4:1 3:1 2½:1 2:1 1½:1

Slope of apron

radians

Swash heights for various uniform apron slopes and berm widths—smooth impervious facings

the berm is less than 0·15 of the wave length. In view of the value of this method to the designer, Thorndike Saville's paper has, with his permission, and that of the U.S. Army Coastal Engineering Research Center, Corps of Engineers, and the Council on Wave Research, been reproduced in the Appendix on pp. 17–26.

1.11 WAVE PRESSURES

Gaillard's experiments showed that, using metric units, the maximum pressure exerted in Mg/m^2 by breaking waves on a sea wall is $0·068\ (V+V_m)^2$, where V is the wave velocity (unbroken) in m/sec, and V_m is the orbital velocity, in m/sec, at the crest equal to $\pi H/P$.

Alternatively, Little gives, using metric units, the velocity of waves breaking in shallow water as $3·2\ \sqrt{D_1}$, where D_1 is the height of the crest above the sea bed in metres; and by analogy, with the force exerted by change of momentum as a result of a jet of water impinging on a plate, he derived a simple expression which in metric units gives $p = 3·59H$ for the pressure in Mg/m^2 exerted by breaking waves on maritime works. This formula is applicable to the most usual case of short waves and beach and wall slopes exceeding 1 in 50 (vertical to horizontal). To make some allowance for long waves he suggests, using metric units, the use of the expression $p = 4·49H$, H being the wave height in metres out at sea. Wave pressures for various wave heights may be read directly from Design Chart F. In the general case Little's expression undoubtedly overestimates the pressure but it is useful for preliminary assessments.

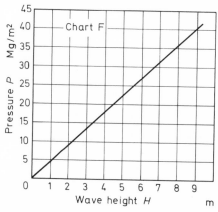

Wave pressures corresponding to various wave heights

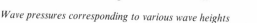

The velocity of water moving forward from the crest of a breaking wave is about twice the velocity of the wave, and local damage is most likely to occur if the sea wall takes the full force of this jet. Intense pressures may also result if the breaking waves enclose pockets of air against the wall. These may cause failure where, because of cracks or other openings in the apron, high pneumatic pressures develop under the apron and blow out the wall as the wave recedes.

When the waves are reflected and do not break, the pressure exerted by the clapotis is about equal to that which would result from still water against the wall raised to the same height as the top of the clapotis.

The effects of waves on the inshore sea bed and on the foreshore are dealt with in Chapter 2.

1.12 WAVE DATA

Wherever possible, design should be based on long-term observed data, particularly in shallowing waters where accurate prediction is difficult (see Bretschneider's paper of 1957).

Valuable data may be obtained from a wave gauge (a graduated pole erected on the foreshore so that with binoculars the rise and fall of the surface of the sea may be observed). From this the height of the waves may be estimated. The wave period can be determined by timing with a stop watch the rise and fall of patches of foam or of the surface of the sea at the wave gauge. The tide level is best found from gauge board readings in a tidal basin or from recorders on nearby maritime structures.

On beach foreshores the wave height may also be roughly estimated from the height of the shingle full by using the expressions given in section 1.10 for swash height.

1.13 WIND FORCE

Wind force and direction are of importance to sea defence engineers and in meteorological reports the strength of the wind is usually given in accordance with the Beaufort scale (Table 1).

TABLE 1

Force (Beaufort Scale)	Sea Miles (6080 ft) per hour	Kilometres per hour	Wind
0	0–1	0–2	
1–2	2–6	4–11	
3	7–10	13–18	Light
4	11–16	20–30	
5	17–21	32–39	Moderate
6	22–27	41–50	
7	28–33	52–61	Strong
8	34–40	63–74	
9	41–47	76–87	Gale
10	48–55	89–102	
11	56–65	104–120	Storm
12	over 65	120	Hurricane

BIBLIOGRAPHY

Admiralty Tide Tables (Annual), H.M.S.O.

Admiralty Manual of Tides, H.M.S.O.

Waves and Tides, R. C. H. Russell and D. H. MacMillan; Hutchinson

Shore Protection Planning and Design, Beach Erosion Board, Washington, 1954

Design of Sea Defence Works in Relation to Height of Tide and Degree of Exposure, C. H. Dobbie, *Conference on North Sea Floods*, 1953; Instn. Civ. Engrs.

Bitumen in Hydraulic Engineering, W. F. Van Asbeck; Shell Petroleum Co.

Beach Formation by Waves: Some Model Experiments in a Wave Tank, R. A. Bagnold. *J. Instn. Civ. Engrs.* Nov. 1940

Modification of the Sea Bed with a view to Concentration and Dispersal of Sea Waves, F. Vasco Costa and J. Fiuza Perestrelo, *Dock and Harbour Authority* No. 460 Vol. XXXIX Feb. 1959 (Based on an article published in the Portuguese Journal *Tecnica* No. 283, June 1958)

Revisions in Wave Forecasting: Deep and Shallow Water, C. L. Bretschneider, *Proc. Sixth International Conference on Coastal Engineering*, 1957, University of Florida, pub. by the U.S. Council on Wave Research, University of California

Model Investigation on Wave Run-up carried out in the Netherlands during the past Twenty Years, F. Wassing, *Proc. Sixth International Conference on Coastal Engineering*, 1957, University of Florida, pub. by the U.S. Council on Wave Research, University of California

Wave Run-up on Composite Slopes, Thorndike Saville Jr., *Proc. Sixth International Conference on Coastal Engineering*, 1957, University of Florida, pub. by the U.S. Council on Wave Research, University of California

Effect of Berm on Wave Run-up on Composite Beaches, J. B. Herbich and R. M. Sorensen, *J. Waterways & Harbours Div.*, A.S.C.E. Vol. 89, No. WW2, Part I, May 1963

Harbours and Docks, D. H. Little, *Civil Engineering Reference Book*, ed. by Probst and Comrie; Butterworths Scientific Publications

Wind Action on a Water Surface, J. R. D. Francis, *Proc. Instn. Civ. Engrs.* Feb. 1959

Wind Waves, B. Kinsman; Prentice-Hall, 1965

Coastal Hydraulics, A. M. Muir Wood; Macmillan, 1969

Computation of Storm Waves and Swell, R. Silvester and S. Vongvisessomjai, *Proc. Instn. Civ. Engrs.* Feb. 1971

APPENDIX TO CHAPTER 1

[Reproduced from the *Proc. Sixth International Conference on Coastal Engineering*, 1957, University of Florida, published by U.S. Council on Wave Research, University of California.]

WAVE RUN-UP ON COMPOSITE SLOPES

THORNDIKE SAVILLE, Jr.
U.S. Army Coastal Engineering Research Center (formerly the U.S. Beach Erosion Board), Corps of Engineers, Department of the Army

Accurate design data on the height of wave run-up is needed to determine design crest elevations of protective structures subject to wave action such as sea walls, beach fills, and dams. Such structures are normally designed to prevent wave overtopping with consequent flooding on the landward side and, if of an earth type, possible failure by rear face erosion. Wave run-up (the vertical height to which water from a breaking wave will rise on the structure face) therefore has an important bearing on the final determination of crest elevation or freeboard.

Apart from the safety factor, decisions as to the necessary crest elevation frequently have considerable economic implication also, as for example in the levees presently being designed for protection with the planned raised water levels in Lake Okeechobee (Florida) where it has been estimated that each additional foot of levee elevation required will cost several million dollars.

Much study by models has recently been devoted to the problem of run-up on structures, both in this country and abroad. The problem for smooth impermeable structures of constant slope has been discussed previously[1]. Savage[2], more recently, has given data on run-up on roughened and permeable structures, but still of a constant slope. Some information has also been given[1] for composite slopes made up of a smooth impermeable structure slope rising from a smooth 1 on 10 (beach) slope which is at or below the still-water level. Few structures, however, fit exactly the cases reported, and interpolation or extrapolation of the curves is relatively difficult. Consequently resort frequently is still made to an exact model study of a planned structure to obtain the design values of wave run-up. This is particularly the case where more complex composite slope structures, such as those with berms, are being considered.

However, an analysis of existing data shows that this information may be used to predict relatively accurate values of wave run-up for any slope if the actual composite slope is replaced by a hypothetical single constant slope; this hypothetical slope is obtained from the breaking depth and an

17

estimated value of wave run-up. Such a case is shown in *Figure 3* where a composite slope consisting of a beach slope, a very gently sloping berm, and a steep structure slope is replaced (dashed line) by a single hypothetical slope extending from the breaking point to an arbitrarily estimated point of maximum run-up. Using this hypothetical slope, a value of run-up may be determined by interpolation from the earlier data. In the general case, the value of run-up determined will be somewhat different from that initially chosen to obtain the hypothetical single slope; the process is then repeated using the new

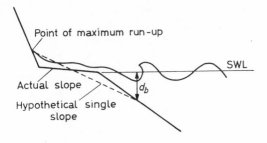

*Figure 3. Schematic of hypothetical single slope for use
in determining run-up for composite slopes*

value of run-up to obtain a new single slope value, which in turn determines a new value of run-up. The process is repeated until identical values are obtained for two successive trials.

In order to make the interpolation between the earlier curves somewhat simpler, these curves have been re-plotted as shown in *Figure 4*. The case of structure depth, that is depth of water at the toe of the structure, between one and three wave heights is the only one presented, as this range contains the breaking point which would be at the toe of the hypothetical single slope structure used here. The figure shows relative run-up (R/H'_0) as a function of structure slope for various values of wave steepness (H'_0/T^2), where R is the wave run-up (the vertical height above still-water level to which water will rise on the face of the structure), H'_0 is the equivalent deep-water wave height, and T is the wave period. It should be noted that the values are given in terms of the deep-water wave height (corrected for refraction), H'_0. This value, if not known initially, may be obtained from the non-breaking wave height in any depth of water by using tables of functions of d/L_0 (relative depth) as, for example, given by Wiegel[3] and later reproduced by the Council on Wave Research[4] and the Beach Erosion Board[5]; or from the breaking depth or breaking height as given by the solitary wave equations[6]. These, as re-arranged to utilise the generally more available value of wave period, T, rather than the deep-water wave length, L_0, are:

$$d_b = 1 \cdot 28 H_b \text{ and } H'_0 = 1 \cdot 5 d_b (H'_0/T^2)^{1/3}$$

or, in metric units,

$$H'_0 = 2 \cdot 23 d_b (H'_0/T^2)^{1/3}$$

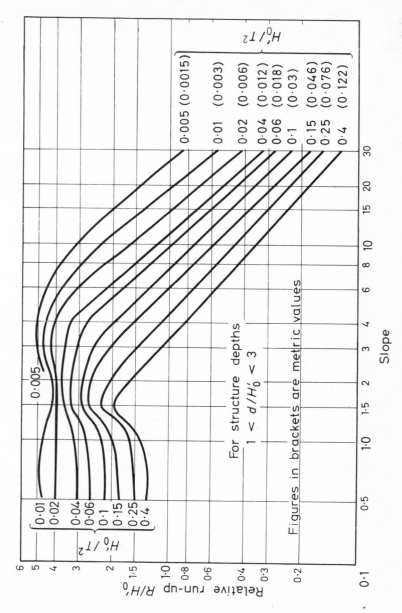

Figure 4. Run-up on sloped structures

where d_b and H_b are respectively the breaking depth and height. These same solitary wave equations may also be used to obtain the breaking depth for use in determining the hypothetical single slope used to replace the actual composite slope.

Although actual verification of this method is not shown until later in the paper, to illustrate the method, an actual design example is worked out below for the Jefferson Parish levee on Lake Ponchartrain outside New Orleans, Louisiana. A schematic diagram of the existing levee is shown in *Figure 5*. The problem was whether this levee would be overtopped by hurricane waves on Lake Ponchartrain, and, if so, how high the existing levee

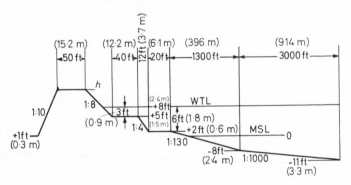

Figure 5. Schematic of Jefferson Parish levee

would have to be raised to prevent overtopping. The wind tide level under hurricane winds for a particular choice of design storm was determined as +8 ft (2·4 m) mean sea level, as indicated on the figure. It was estimated that waves 7 ft (2·1 m) high and of 6·7 sec period would be observed 1 mile (1·6 km) off-shore where the water depth is 19 ft (5·8 m). The equivalent deep-water wave height H'_0 may then be found as 7·38 ft (2·25 m) by obtaining a value of H/H'_0 from tables of functions of d/L_0. For this particular case there are three values of wave run-up that need to be computed. These are: (1) that resulting from the 7 ft (2·1 m) incident wave breaking on the 1 on 130 slope, (2) that from the smaller wave propagated over the 20 ft (6·1 m) berm in 6 ft (1·8 m) of water and breaking on the 1 on 4 slope, and (3) that from the still smaller wave propagated across the 40 ft (12·2 m) berm in 3 ft (0·9 m) of water and breaking directly on the 1 on 8 levee slope. They will be computed below in that order.

(1) *Run-up on 1:8 slope for wave breaking on 1:130 slope:*

Compute $H'_0/T^2 = 0·164 \ (0·05)$

From the solitary wave equation (above) compute the depth of breaking, $d_b = 8·99$ ft (2·74 m)

Assume run-up on the 1:8 slope as any value, say 2 ft (0·61 m)

Compute a hypothetical single slope as a vertical rise from $-0·99$ ft ($-0·30$ m) MSL (breaking depth) to $+10$ ft ($+3·0$ m) (crest of run-up) in a horizontal distance of 40 ft (12·2 m) (1:8 slope = 8 × 5) plus 40 ft (12·2 m) (berm at 3 ft (0·9 m) depth) plus 12 ft (3·7 m) (1:4 slope) plus 20 ft (6·1 m) (berm at 6 ft (1·8 m) depth) plus 389 ft (118·6 m) (1:130 slope = 130×2·99) or slope = 10·99/501 = 1:45·6. From *Figure 4* (extrapolated) determine $R/H'_0 = 0·115$ and compute $R = 0·85$ ft (0·26 m)

Repeat the above computations assuming $R = 0·8$ ft (0·24 m); then slope = 9·79/491·4 = 1:50·2

From *Figure 4* (extrapolated) determine $R/H'_0 = 0·11$; then $R = 0·8$ ft (0·24 m) approximately. As the computed value of 0·8 ft (0·24 m) agrees with the assumed, then this value is the final computed run-up for these particular assumptions as to breaking condition.

(2) *Run-up on 1 : 8 slope from stable wave on 20 ft (6·1 m) berm where d = 6 ft (1·8 m)*:

From $d_b = 6$ ft (1·8 m) using the solitary wave equation, and the same wave period, $T = 6·7$ sec, compute $H'_0 = 4·02$ ft (1·23 m) and $H'_0/T^2 = 0·0895$ (0·027)

Assume the wave breaks just at the toe of 1 : 4 slope

Assume run-up as any value, say, 4 ft (1·22 m)

Compute a hypothetical single slope as a vertical rise from +2 ft (+0·61 m) MSL (depth of breaking) to +12 ft (+3·7 m) (crest of run-up) in a horizontal distance of 12 ft (3·7 m) (1:4 slope) plus 40 ft (12·2 m) (berm) plus 56 ft (17·1 m) (1:8 slope = 8×7) or slope = 10/108 = 1:10·8

From *Figure 4*, $R/H'_0 = 0·71$ and $R = 2·85$ ft (0·87 m)

Assume $R = 2·85$ ft (0·87 m) and repeat, computing slope = 8·85/98·8 = 1:11·2 and $R/H'_0 = 0·68$ from which $R = 2·74$ ft (0·84 m)

Assume $R = 2·74$ ft (0·84 m) and repeat, computing R again = 2·74 ft (0·84 m), which becomes the final run-up value.

(3) *Run-up on 1 : 8 slope from stable wave on 40 ft (12·2 m) berm where d = 3 ft (0·9 m)*:

From $d_b = 3$ ft (0·9 m) and $T = 6·7$ sec, compute $H'_0 = 1·43$ ft (0·44 m), and $H'_0/T^2 = 0·0318$ (0·0097).

From *Figure 4*, $R/H'_0 = 1·67$ and $R = 2·39$ ft (0·73 m).

The design run-up for this wave condition is then the maximum of these three values or 2·74 ft (0·84 m). It may be noted that this value is not for the

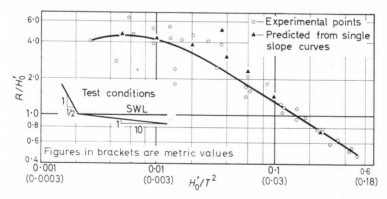

Figure 6. Wave run-up, composite slope (1:½ above SWL, 1:10 below SWL)

full sized hurricane wave breaking on the outer slope, but for a somewhat smaller wave in the spectrum (or a reformed wave) which can propagate as a stable wave over the deeper berm, and break on the 1:4 slope.

Comparisons have been made for values computed by this method with those determined experimentally in wave flumes for certain cases. These are composite slopes made up of smooth constant impermeable slopes of 1 on 6, 1 on 3, 1 on $1\frac{1}{2}$, and 1 on $\frac{1}{2}$ above still-water level and a constant beach slope of 1 on 10 below still-water level. The comparisons for these cases are shown in *Figures 6–9*. The experimental data and curves for the 1 on 6, 1 on 3, and 1 on $1\frac{1}{2}$ slopes are those previously reported Saville[1], and data for the 1 on $\frac{1}{2}$ slope are additional unpublished data obtained at the Beach Erosion Board; the curves in all cases were drawn by eye through the general centre of the experimental points. Actually the points determined by the hypothetical slope method may be connected to form a curve which can be compared with the experimental curve. As the plotted points represent dimensionless

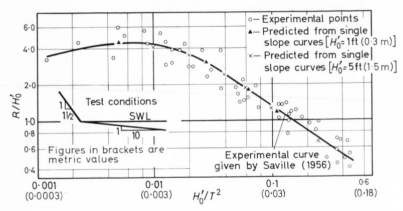

Figure 7. *Wave run-up, composite slope (1 : 1½ above SWL, 1 : 10 below SWL)*

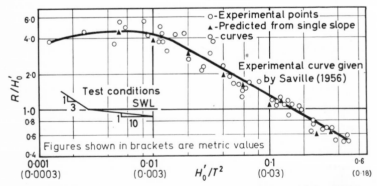

Figure 8. *Wave run-up, composite slope (1 : 3 above SWL, 1 : 10 below SWL)*

quantities the actual wave height used in determining the points makes no difference in the curves obtained. This may be seen in *Figure 7* where values determined from waves of both 1 and 5 ft (0·3 and 1·5 m) height are shown. The points or curves predicted by this method vary from somewhat above the experimental curve for the 1 on $\frac{1}{2}$ slope, to almost exactly on the curve for the 1 on $1\frac{1}{2}$ slope, to somewhat below the curve for the 1 on 3 and 1 on 6 slopes. In every case, however, the predicted points lie within the scatter pattern of the experimental points. The deviation of the predicted values from the previously drawn experimental curves is generally within 10 per cent with a maximum deviation of about 25 per cent.

In addition, a comparison was made with run-up data for a number of structures having berms. These comparisons are shown in *Figure 10*, where the actual prototype value of predicted run-up is compared with the experimentally determined values from model studies for the Lake Okeechobee levee design reported by Hudson, Jackson and Cuckler[7]; and for beach dune design reported by Savage[2,8]. The former were tests made at the Waterways Experiment Station of the Corps of Engineers in Vicksburg, Mississippi, and involved underwater slopes (a_1) of 1 on 3 and 1 on 6, berms of 30, 50 and 70 ft

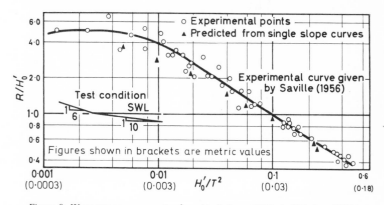

Figure 9. Wave run-up, composite slope (1:6 above SWL, 1:10 below SWL)

(9·1, 15·2 and 21·3 m) width on a 1 on 20 slope with the toe at still-water level, and upper structure slopes of 1 on 3 (see *Figure 10*). Those reported by Savage were tests carried out at the Beach Erosion Board and involved an underwater beach slope of 1 on 20, horizontal berms of 50 and 150 ft (15·2 and 45·7 m) width, and dune slopes of 1 on 5 and 1 on 10 (see *Figure 10*). There was also an outer bar involved in these latter tests; the values used herein were restricted to the cases where the wave did not break on passing over the bar. Waves breaking on the bar could also have been used, but additional computations would have been necessary to determine whether the run-up was due to the wave breaking on the bar or to the reformed waves generated in the water area shoreward of the bar. Similarly usage was also restricted to the cases of still-water depths over the berm of −2, −1, 0, and 1 ft (−0·6, −0·3, 0 and 0·3 m) in an attempt to ensure that the run-up was due to the wave breaking on the beach slope rather than to a reformed smaller wave propagating in the water over the berm.

As may be noted from *Figure 10*, the agreement of the predicted with the experimental values is fairly good except for the case of the 150 ft (45·7 m) berm, where experimental values were considerably higher than those predicted. It is interesting to note that for these cases essentially the same value of run-up was obtained for both the 50 ft (15·2 m) and 150 ft (45·7 m) berm width. The maximum difference between the two was 0·2 ft (0·06 m) for run-ups ranging from 1·9 to 4·2 ft (0·58 to 1·28 m). This would seem to imply that

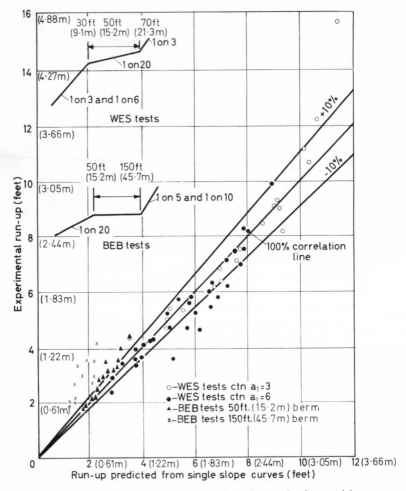

Figure 10. Comparison with experimental values of run-up for slopes with berms obtained by single slope method

after a berm has reached a certain width, further widening has no significant effect in reducing wave run-up—at least for horizontal berms. This possibility has previously been indicated by researchers in the Netherlands[9] in stating that berms wider than about one-fourth of the wave length, while still reducing the wave uprush, do so at a lesser rate. For the tests reported here one-fourth of the wave length is between 40 and 50 ft (12·2 and 15·2 m). This reduction in effect of berm width may be because, in the laboratory tests at least, a definite 'set-up' of water occurred on the berm. This 'set-up' or increase in mean water level is caused by the forward transport of water by the waves and, for these tests, ranged between 0·9 and 2·4 ft (0·27 and 0·73 m) with an average value of 1·7 ft (0·52 m) and a most frequent value of 1·8 ft (0·55 m). This 'set-up' increased the water depth over the berm appreciably, and in many cases the run-up measured may have been due more to reformed waves or surges in this increased depth than to the actual uprush of the wave. This is partially substantiated by the fact that experimental values for the higher berms (at or above still-water level) are more nearly approached by the predicted values than are those for the lower berms where a greater water depth is observed. This 'set-up' phenomenon appears to be much more apparent for horizontal berms than for sloping berms, where the water pushed forward by the wave may flow back much more readily. No mention of this occurrence was made in the Vicksburg tests, and the difference between predicted and observed values for these tests did not appear to be affected by the berm width (which varied from 30 to 70 ft (9·1 to 21·3 m)).

Referring again to *Figure 10*, some 72 per cent of the experimental values lie within ±10 per cent of the predicted values if the points for the 150 ft (45·7 m) berm are ignored; if these points are included, then 61 per cent of the experimental values are within ±10 per cent of the predicted.

In conclusion, a method for predicting wave run-up on any type of composite sloped impermeable structure has been presented. The accuracy of the method, as judged by comparison with experimentally observed values obtained from laboratory tests, is regarded as satisfactory. It is felt that use of the method will simplify design determination of run-up for many structures. However, further tests are needed to define those cases where width of horizontal berm becomes great enough to affect the validity of the method.

ACKNOWLEDGMENT

The work described herein was carried out as part of a broad research programme of the Beach Erosion Board of the United States Army Corps of Engineers. Permission for publication granted by the Chief of Engineers is appreciated.

REFERENCES

1. SAVILLE, T., JR. (1956). Wave Run-up on Shore Structures. *Proc. Amer. Soc. Civ. Engrs., Separate No. 925, Jour. Waterways Div.,* V. 82, No. WW2.
2. SAVAGE, R. P. (1958). Wave Run-up on Roughened and Permeable Slopes. *Proc. Amer. Civ. Engrs., Separate No.* 1640, *Jour. Waterways Div.,* V. 84, No. WW3
3. WIEGEL, R. L. (1948). Oscillatory Waves. *Bulletin, Beach Erosion Board, Special Issue No.* 1
4. WIEGEL, R. L. (1954). *Gravity Waves, Tables of Functions.* Council on Wave Research, Engineering Foundation
5. Beach Erosion Board (1954). Shore Protection Planning and Design. *Beach Erosion Board Technical Report No.* 4
6. MUNK, W. H. (1949). The Solitary Wave Theory and its Application to Surf Problems. *Ann. N.Y. Acad. Sci.,* Vol. 51, Art. 3, pp. 376–424
7. HUDSON, R. Y., JACKSON, R. A. and CUCKLER, R. E. (1957). Wave Run-up and Overtopping, Levee Sections, Lake Okeechobee, Florida. *Waterways Experiment Station, Technical Report No.* 2–449
8. SAVAGE, R. P. (1957). Model Tests of Wave Run-up for Hurricane Project. *Bulletin, Beach Erosion Board,* V. 11, No. 1, pp. 1–12
9. VAN ASBECK, W. F., FERGUSON, H. A. and SCHOEMAKER, H. J. (1953). New Design of Breakwaters and Seawalls with Special Reference to Slope Protection: *XVIIIth International Navigation Congress, Rome,* Section II, Question I, pp. 169–198

Additional references which have appeared since publication of this article
10. SAVILLE, T., JR. (1962). An approximation of the Wave Run-up Frequency Distribution, *Proc. Eighth International Conf. on Coastal Engineering*
11. HERBICH, J. B. and SORENSEN, R. M. (May 1963). Effect of Berm on Wave Run-up on Composite Beaches, *J. Waterways & Harbours, Div.,* A.S.C.E., Vol. 89, No. WW2, Part I
12. VAN OORSCHOT, J. H. and D'AUGREMOND, K. (1968). The Effect of Wave Energy Spectra on Wave Run-up. *Proc. Eleventh Int. Conf. on Coastal Engineering*

Chapter 2

Natural Sea Defences

2.1 GENERAL

A characteristic of sand and shingle foreshores is permeability and this quality is an important factor in foreshore stability. Any impermeable surface introduced tends to alter this stability and hence the advisability of using, when possible, permeable defences where artificial works are required to aid, strengthen and supplement natural foreshores. Permeable groynes (*Figures 11–14*) are an example of transverse structures of this kind, and wave screens (*Figure 14*), tetrapod walls (*Figure 15*) and similar permeable revetments (*Figures 13, 16* and *17*) are examples of longitudinal ones.

The maintenance and strengthening of natural sea defences are the first aims of the sea defence engineer. Indeed unless the foreshore can be (or becomes) stabilised by one means or another there is no end to the additional works required on a sea wall as the foreshore drops, exposing the toe, and as the greater depths of water in front of the wall allow bigger waves to break with greater impact on it.

2.2 EFFECTS OF WAVES ON FORESHORES

Seaward of the plunge line (where the waves break) shingle on the bed is not generally moved by waves in depths much greater than the wave height (it can of course be moved by strong tidal streams in greater depths) but sand on the bed is moved by waves for a considerable distance offshore, the distance depending on the depth of the water, the grain size, the height and period of the waves.

Long low waves cause a net landward drift along the bed and a net seaward drift at the surface. The movement at the bed caused by a long solitary wind-generated wave is a rapid forward stroke and

27

Figure 11. Timber permeable groyne on shingle foreshore at Pett

Figure 12. Mobbs-type steel permeable groyne at Walcott

*Figure 13. Block-filled timber revetment and Mobbs-type
steel permeable groyne at Mundesley*

Figure 14. Pett wave screen, timber barrier and permeable groyne

Figure 15. Tetrapods—Marine Drive sea wall, Bombay

Figure 16. Block-filled timber revetment at Christchurch

Figure 17. Timber permeable revetment at Mundesley

a slow backward stroke, and this can cause movement of shingle in depths greater than indicated above. An onshore wind moving the sea surface landwards will tend to cause an offshore drift on the bed, particularly where the waves are steep. Thus it is that sand foreshores usually accrete during the summer months under the influence of long low waves and drop during the winter under the action of steep storm waves with onshore winds. As will be seen later, the sand that is drawn down under these conditions is drawn into an area where the rate of littoral drift is much less than on the upper part of the foreshore, so that under subsequent favourable conditions it will tend to return to the upper foreshore.

The effect of offshore sandbanks is to absorb some of the wave energy approaching the coast and to alter to some extent tidal currents.

From the foregoing it will be seen that the chief cause of movement of sand and shingle is the breaking wave, so that the main movement is above low water and along the foreshore in the direction of the breaking wave, the sand being carried partly in suspension and partly along the bed and the shingle by rolling along the bed. In the case of sand considerable movement can also be caused by the action of the wind on the exposed dried portion of the surface. The height to which the swash rises and carries the shingle is discussed in section 1.10. Since the beach is permeable, far less water returns down the surface than goes up it, so that the effect of swash is to build up the shingle. The slope is therefore a function of the permeability, the less permeable the material the flatter the slope; thus, the slope of shingle may be 1 in 7 (depending on its size) whilst that of sand may be of the order of 1 in 25, or 1 in 50.

2.3 EFFECT OF IMPERMEABLE STRUCTURES ON FORESHORE STABILITY

In section 2.2 it was seen that the less permeable the material the flatter the slope. The effect of impermeable structures has therefore to be carefully considered.

In an experiment carried out by Bagnold, beach material was heaped against a vertical concrete back wall and the wave height was gradually increased until the water surging up the beach reached the vicinity of the wall. It was found that the presence of the wall caused a breakdown to occur before the free water of the surge actually touched the wall above the shingle, the beach breaking down and falling from a slope of 22° to 14°.

In another experiment a steel plate was inserted at a slope of about 1 in 2 just below the sloping beach surface. It was found to act in the same way as the vertical wall had done, the beach breaking down and falling from a slope of 22° to 14°.

In both cases the changes were evidently caused by the impermeable wall preventing free percolation of the water through the material.

An experiment carried out by Inglis and Russell indicated the effect of vertical walls on sand foreshores. Fine sand was laid and allowed to become stable under the action of waves of constant height and of fluctuating tidal levels of constant range. When the profile had become stable a vertical plate representing a sea wall was inserted at a point between high water and the highest point reached by the swash. As the experiment continued the level of the sand against the sea wall fell and after about 35 tides it had fallen from above high-water level to below low-water level.

The effect of an impermeable apron in flattening the slope of shingle is not usually a serious matter since the change in slope is not very great and the same total volume of shingle remains in front of the wall to absorb wave impact. In the case of sand the effect is much more serious and it appears that the flatter the slope of the wall the less severe is the disturbance to the foreshore. Interesting information in this connection is given in section 4.3. At the present time insufficient data are available on this important aspect of wall design and more research on it would be very welcome.

2.4 LITTORAL DRIFT

Littoral drift, termed littoral transport in the United States where the material moved is referred to as the littoral drift, is the aggregate movement of material along the coast (in English usage littoral drift can also mean the material moved). Its direction is determined by strength, duration and direction of winds and the fetches corresponding to the wind directions. If the prevailing wind comes from the direction of the shortest fetch then it is unlikely that the direction of the drift will be that of the prevailing wind.

On the south coast of England the prevailing wind comes from the south-west and as this is also the direction of the longest fetch the littoral drift is generally eastward. The rate of drift is naturally affected by the angle of the coastline to the waves. A reverse movement may, however, prevail, for instance where a land promontory gives protection from the west. This phenomenon is, for example, created by the shingle promontory of Dungeness (see *Figure 18*) so that the drift is westward between Littlestone and Greatstone which are on the east side of Dungeness. On the east coast of England the drift has in the past been predominantly southerly.

In some circumstances it could be possible for the shingle drift to be in one direction and the sand drift in the other (in the case of sand drift the movement of sand by the wind must, of course, never be overlooked—see section 2.7). For example, because of the shielding effect of a headland or because the fetch is short only small waves may reach a shore from the direction of the prevailing wind,

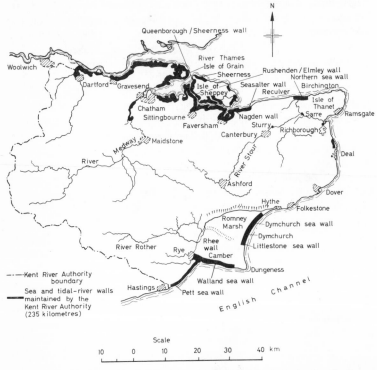

Figure 18. Plan showing the location of Sea Defence Works maintained by the Kent River Authority

and these would move sand but not shingle. Winds from opposing directions, on the other hand, may generate larger waves and therefore cause shingle drift in the direction opposite to that of the sand drift.

The drift does not necessarily cause erosion of the foreshore, it may equally cause accretion; it is changes in the rate of drift that are significant. Since the angle of the waves to the shore affects the rate of drift, there will be a tendency for erosion or accretion to occur where the line of the shore changes direction. The determining factors are the rate of arrival and the rate of departure of beach material over the length of foreshore considered. Coast erosion by wave action is not always the only source of foreshore material, for some evidence suggests it is possible for strong tidal currents in particular circumstances to feed beaches from offshore. There are, however, no known cases of this kind on the Kent coast.

Littoral drift of both sand and shingle can exhibit an undulating character, that is to say a large body of material in the form of a hump can move along the coast. The cause of this is not clearly understood.

2.5 GROYNES

It was seen in section 2.2 that the movement of material along the coast affecting the foreshore is mainly above low water. It is greatest in the vicinity of high water and hence one of the difficulties of accreting sand on low foreshores at levels where the rate of movement is much less. Groynes are used to limit the movement of material, and to stabilise the foreshore. This combats erosion and encourages accretion. It is generally impracticable to construct groynes that will halt all drift, and since, therefore, normal groynes cannot prevent all loss of material, in the long run they are useless unless natural or artificial feed is available to replace the material that is lost. With limited feed, high groynes usually have the effect of forming the shingle bank very irregularly, and from the amenity aspect they are disadvantageous. They are also costly, and as a result low groynes are more usual these days for shingle as well as for sand foreshores.

On shingle beaches the head of the groyne is preferably taken either a short distance landward of the shingle full or into the upper part of the sea wall, whilst on sand foreshores where the sand is usually well below high water the landward end of the groyne terminates at the lower part of the sea wall.

Where the groynes are used to hold shingle they are carried seawards only a short distance beyond the toe of the shingle. The distance seawards that groynes designed to hold sand are extended depends on the feed and the build-up required. If the feed is not great they are taken down to low water in order to trap as much material as possible; if the feed is good they can sometimes be made a little shorter, particularly if the build-up required is small, otherwise the groyne will not be long enough to provide the gradient needed for the build-up at the landward end. Unless special circumstances exist, in practice, low water is taken to be low-water neap tides. The cost of groyne construction greatly increases seaward of low-water neaps.

The accumulative effect of the normal type of solid groyne is to build up material on the side from which the material is coming and to cause erosion on the other side until the accretion tops the groyne and material passes over (or round the seaward end) to commence filling the next compartment. In calm conditions with small directly onshore waves the effect on a sand foreshore is to even up the distribution of sand within the groyne compartments.

The Hydraulics Research Station basic coastal model represented an idealised version of the foreshore to the south of Southwold Harbour and the results are qualitatively applicable to prototype sands ranging from 0·15 to 0·45 mm mean grain size (on the Dymchurch foreshore the sand ranges from about 0·125 to 0·33 mm, being mainly about 0·17 mm). The results of the experiments apply best to foreshores where the sand is somewhat coarser than that typically found on British coasts.

Solid groynes 3 ft (1 m) high, 180 ft (55 m) long and 180 ft (55 m) apart reduced the quantity of littoral drift to one-eighth of its former value, but also resulted in a loss of sand from the upper part of the foreshore. Solid groynes 18 in (0·5 m) high, 180 ft (55 m) long and 360 ft (110 m) apart reduced the littoral drift to half and did not cause a loss of sand from the upper foreshore. It was found that there was no loss of sand if the sand built up to the top of the groynes, but that if the sand did not do this then a loss occurred. It was therefore inferred that for the conditions reproduced in the experiments low widely spaced groynes were to be preferred.

In some of the experiments there was a loss of sand from the foreshore and a corresponding accumulation offshore. In no case was there a gain of sand and a corresponding loss offshore.

The experiments were made with waves the equivalent of 2 ft (0·6 m) high in deep water which rose to 3 ft (1 m) before breaking and always approached obliquely from the same direction. The tidal range reproduced was 6 ft (2 m) and the tidal currents reached a maximum equivalent to 2 ft/sec (0·6 m/sec) in both directions.

The Hydraulics Research Station investigations showed that the littoral drift was greatest in the vicinity of the high water contour and less than one-tenth of that there along the low water contour.

With the very flat slope of sand (as distinct from that of shingle) it must always be borne in mind that the effect of groynes where they accrete at very low levels must be to lay the sand at artificially steep slopes. It must be frankly admitted that the way groynes affect low sand foreshores (if indeed in many cases there is any material effect) is obscure and much research will be necessary before a complete understanding is reached.

Groynes are commonly constructed at right angles to the shore and at spacings equal to their lengths. The angle and the spacing on any foreshore eventually become fixed as the result of long experience determining the most efficient arrangement. Shorter intermediate groynes are often placed between the main groynes. On foreshores where there has been no previous experience of groyning works it is as a general rule better to commence with groynes at spacings equal to one and a half times to twice the

Figure 19. Northern sea wall type Q

length of the groynes and to later increase the number of groynes, if necessary, in the light of the results obtained.

In the tests carried out by the Hydraulics Research Station, with the groynes aligned at an angle of 18° from the normal with their offshore ends in the 'down-drift direction, no measurable difference was found from the experiment with the groynes normal to the shore. With the groynes pointing towards the origin of the littoral drift, the results were very similar, except that erosion down-drift of each groyne was greater than with normal groynes and this tended to endanger the stability of the groynes.

Construction of groynes is normally commenced at the end furthest from the direction from which the feed is coming. Where possible, it is advisable to begin the construction on a length where accretion is taking place in order to reduce the problem of the terminal groyne to a minimum. To allow the foreshore to build up relatively uniformly it is customary to commence with no more than two planks at each groyne above foreshore level and to plank up one or two boards at a time above the material as the foreshore accretes. Artificial replenishment down-drift of the terminal groyne will generally be necessary; alternatively, the new groyne compartments can be filled (see section 2.6). Within the groyne compartments the material tends to become orientated so that it faces directly the on-coming waves.

Figure 19 shows a type of groyne suitable for sand or shingle. Construction normally comprises half-round oak piles (approx. 300 mm diameter) at 1·75 m centres, 2·5–3·0 m long, penetration 1·5–1·75 m, supporting 225 × 75 mm planks fixed to the piles with 10 mm galvanised spikes, 150 mm long, or 20 mm bolts. The depth that the planks are taken below foreshore level depends on the degree of foreshore variation anticipated.

Figures 20 (a) and *20 (b)* show another type of groyne, particularly suitable for sand foreshores. The timber sheet piles are to prevent under-run.

Figures 21(a) and *21(b)* show the popular type of groyne designed by Edward Case and first constructed by him at Dymchurch in 1894. These are very suitable for predominantly sand foreshores.

Under very exposed conditions land ties are sometimes used to strengthen timber groynes and *Figure 22* illustrates the use of these at Eastbourne.

Salt water prevents attack by fungi (except marine fungi which only slightly soften and do not seriously harm the wood), so that the qualities that have to be borne in mind in choosing suitable timbers are: resistance to abrasion (particularly on shingle beaches), resistance to marine borers (where these are present), ease of working, and cost. The hardwoods, jarrah, greenheart and oak, are resistant to abrasion and to some extent to attack by marine borers, but are less easy to work than softwoods. B.C. pine is a popular softwood for groyne construction; it is cheap, easy to work and is suitable for sand foreshores where it will not be subjected to much shingle abrasion. If the presence of marine borers is known or suspected softwoods can be made resistant to attack by pressure creosoting (incised full cell process) or by similar treatment with proprietary chemical preservatives. These latter have the advantage that the timber is 'clean' for handling after treatment.

A number of experimental timber permeable groynes have been constructed on shingle foreshores on the east and south coasts of Kent (see *Figures 11, 14* and *23*). These groynes appear to have the effect of retarding the longitudinal velocity component of the

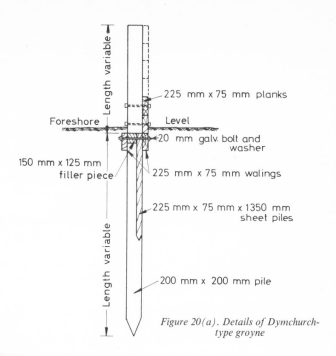

225 mm x 75 mm planks

Foreshore   Level

20 mm galv. bolt and washer

150 mm x 125 mm filler piece

225 mm x 75 mm walings

225 mm x 75 mm x 1350 mm sheet piles

200 mm x 200 mm pile

Length variable

Figure 20(a). Details of Dymchurch-type groyne

Figure 20(b). Dymchurch-type groyne

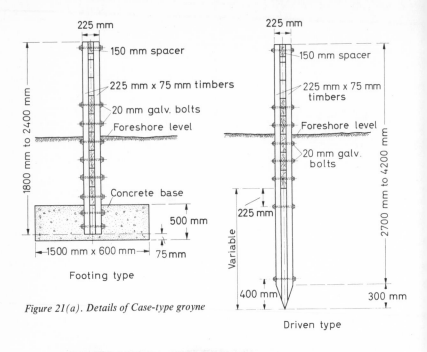

225 mm

150 mm spacer

225 mm x 75 mm timbers

20 mm galv. bolts

Foreshore level

1800 mm to 2400 mm

Concrete base

500 mm

1500 mm x 600 mm

75 mm

Footing type

Figure 21(a). Details of Case-type groyne

225 mm

150 mm spacer

225 mm x 75 mm timbers

Foreshore level

20 mm galv. bolts

2700 mm to 4200 mm

225 mm

Variable

400 mm

300 mm

Driven type

Figure 21(b). Case-type groyne on foreshore at Dymchurch

Figure 22. Groyne with land ties at Eastbourne

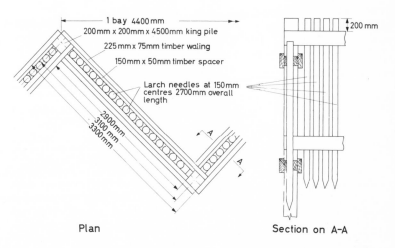

Plan

Section on A-A

Figure 23. Details of timber permeable groyne

breaking wave and the swash, and hence slowing down the rate of littoral movement. Unlike conventional solid groynes, whilst they impede the shingle drift at the same time they allow pebbles to pass through and so reduce scour on the sides remote from the direction from which the material is coming. The effect is then to build up the beach for considerable distances on either side of the groyne.

The authors are of the opinion that, in general, these groynes are not superior to conventional solid groynes but that in some particular circumstances their use may be preferred. For example: (a) on very exposed positions where there may be a danger of conventional groynes being damaged and washed out; (b) on very isolated lengths where the cost of planking and de-planking conventional groynes would be excessive; or, (c) as terminal groynes combined, as necessary, with artificial feed where the typical scour created on the down-drift side of solid groynes would not be acceptable.

On one length on the east coast of Kent the practice is to partly block up the openings in the permeable groynes below beach level allowing water but not shingle through.

No permeable groynes on sand foreshores have been built in Kent but they have been constructed on the Norfolk coast by S. W. Mobbs, C.Eng., F.I.Mun.E., the pioneer in this field, and some of these may be seen in *Figures 12* and *13*. Those in *Figure 13* were constructed at Mundesley in 1958 in conjunction with the permeable revetment shown, and within a short time this foreshore attained a level 4 ft (1·2 m) above the 1953 level.

So far the results of model tests at the Hydraulics Research Station on permeable groynes for sand foreshores have not been encouraging. Hydraulics Research Paper No. 3 says: 'According to Mr. Mobbs the accumulation begins several hundred feet up-drift of the first groyne raising a bar of fine sand near the low water mark, which extends along the system. The bar moves slowly inshore to build up the upper beach. This behaviour could not have been reproduced in the model at H.R.S. because the zone where the accumulation might first have taken place was outside the limits of the model.'

At the present time too little is known about groynes of this type, but the authors feel that whilst there are doubtless some circumstances where such groynes can be used with advantage (for example on lengths of coast where there is a great deal of material in movement), they are not convinced that in general they are likely to replace solid groynes on sand foreshores.

2.6 ARTIFICIAL SHINGLE FEED (BEACH RECHARGE)

Artificial building up and feeding of shingle combined with (in many cases but not necessarily in every case) a suitable system of groynes provides a natural permeable defence and if the annual replenishment required is not too great the cost of feeding is often very much less than the total cost of maintaining a sea wall (the construction of which would be an alternative type of sea defence) and the interest on the capital represented by a sea wall. Under such schemes material is transported from where shingle is accreting to lengths where erosion is taking place. The replenishment shingle benefits not only the section of coast where it it placed but also the down-drift coast along which it eventually travels.

It must be borne in mind that unless an eroding foreshore in front of a sea wall is stabilised the inevitable prospect must be faced of extending repeatedly the apron of the wall seawards as the foreshore falls. As the toe of the wall becomes exposed there is usually the added threat that with greater depths of water in front larger waves can break on the wall with greater impact and uprush, Generally speaking, on a deteriorating foreshore shingle drops much more rapidly than sand and the estimated rate of fall determines the extent to which an apron should be extended. For example, if the shingle is dropping rapidly then the apron should be extended to at least sand level.

For design it should be assumed that for stability the top of the shingle fill must be at or slightly above swash height and the seaward profile must be at the known stable slope for the size of shingle used. The swash height taken will be either that observed from the heights of shingle fulls in the vicinity or calculated roughly from the information given in section 1.10.

Artificial replenishment has been carried out for a number of years on the Pett and Walland foreshores. In *Figures 24* and *25* the Walland foreshore may be seen before and after replenishment. The groyne posts were heightened and the shingle was tipped on the foreshore down to low water at intervals along the shore up to about 300 metres and to roughly the final level of the top of the reformed bank. The action of the sea then distributed it along the beach. After this the groynes were dug out and planked up. Annual replenishment along the 4 km length is of the order of 31,000 m³.

Figures 26 and *27* show similar work carried out at Littlestone.

It is possible that with the decreasing costs of mechanical operations the time may come in the future when sea defences will to a great extent consist of artificially created foreshores built up and maintained from suitable material dredged from the offshore sea

Figure 24. Walland foreshore—shingle being tipped

Figure 25. Walland foreshore—after shingle replenishment

Figure 26. Littlestone foreshore before shingle replenishment

Figure 27. Littlestone foreshore after shingle replenishment

bed. The covering of the bed of the north part of the English Channel adjacent to England is estimated to be: mud 1 per cent, sand 56 per cent, shingle 40 per cent, and rock 3 per cent.

2.7 SAND DUNES

Sand by itself may form a foreshore rising above high-water level and this often occurs in bays. It is characteristic of such situations that as the sand is able to dry between tides it is frequently carried still higher and further shorewards by the wind to form the upper part of the foreshore and sand dunes. Thus an adequate sea defence may be formed and examples on the Sussex and Kent coasts may be seen at Camber, near Rye Harbour, and at Greatstone, just east of Dungeness.

Sand dunes may be built up by the construction of permeable screens. These may be of any suitable material and are usually about 1 m high with a total of about 50 per cent of their area open. As the screens become buried further screens are constructed above them and so the dune is built up. A very interesting account and theory of dune building has been given by J. Tuora.

To stabilise the dunes marram grass is planted. Once it is well rooted it collects wind-blown sand, holds it and gradually builds it up. It is unfortunately easily destroyed by pedestrian traffic; hence the need to fence off dunes where possible to prevent damage by the public. *Figure 28*, of Camber sand dunes, shows brushwood faggot screens and newly planted lines of marram grass. *Figure 29* shows established marram grass on these dunes. *Figures 30 (a)* to *30 (d)*, of Greatstone sand dunes, were taken from the footbridge in *Figure 31 (a)* and show the build up of sand following the erection of two rows of wattle fencing. *Figure 31 (b)* shows the amount of accretion that had taken place over a period of seven years.

The shrub buckthorn grows well on sand dunes, it helps to stabilise the sand and its prickly nature acts as a deterrent to those who might damage the dunes. Conifers have also been grown successfully on sand dunes; they are usually planted about 1·5 m apart at the age of 2 or 3 years. As an experiment, grass seed has been sown on the sand dunes at Camber and a short description of this work is given in section 2.11.

2.8 SALTINGS

The value of saltings as sea defences is described in Chapter 4. Rice grass, see *Figure 32*, is used to combat erosion and to build up

Figure 28. Camber sand dunes—brushwood faggot screens and newly planted lines of marram grass

Figure 29. Established marram grass on Camber sand dunes

Figure 30(a). Greatstone sand dunes—first line of wattle fencing

Figure 30(b). Greatstone sand dunes—first line of wattle fencing buried

Figure 30(c). Greatstone sand dunes—second line of wattle fencing

Figure 30(d). Greatstone sand dunes—second line of wattle fencing buried

Figure 31(a). Greatstone sand dunes—timber footbridge just after construction

Figure 31(b). Greatstone sand dunes—timber footbridge showing build-up of dunes

Figure 32. Rice grass on saltings—Harty Ferry, Isle of Sheppey

saltings in front of clay embankments in order to give increased protection from wave action and to support stone pitching that tends to slip into the soft mud that often exists at the toe of such walls.

Rice grass will not grow well if it is covered by water for more than an average of 3–4 hours per tide and it seems to thrive best where the roots are covered only by high spring tides. Plants put in 1 m apart in the spring usually grow into a compact mass in 3–6 years.

2.9 CLIFF EROSION

Works to prevent erosion of friable cliffs are frequently required. The general procedure is to: (a) stabilise and accrete the foreshore by one of the methods described in this chapter, (b) provide if necessary a longitudinal wall to protect the toe of the cliff, this may be permeable or impermeable and take the form of one of the types of wall described in Chapters 4 and 5, (c) grade back the cliff to a stable slope, and (d) provide drains, if necessary, to the graded face.

Figure 33 (a) shows work of this kind combined with amenity features carried out to give protection to the cliffs at Minnis Bay, Birchington. *Figure 17* is of the permeable revetment which com-

Figure 33(a). Cliff protection works combined with amenity features at Minnis Bay, Birchington

Figure 33(b). Graded chalk cliffs at Westgate combined with protective and amenity works

bined with a permeable groyne system protects the cliffs at Mundesley, Norfolk.

Figure 33 (b) shows graded chalk cliffs at Westgate, Kent, combined with protective and amenity works. The cliffs are graded to a minimum angle of 15° to the vertical to minimise the risk of falls caused by frost action and to keep the line of the protective works at the toe of the cliffs as uniform as practicable. These latter works prevent the undermining of the cliffs which would otherwise occur.

For clay cliffs the face is usually graded as necessary to flat slopes of about 4:1 and 'herring-bone' surface rubble drains are provided, the main 'back-bone' drains at about the depth of the slips that have occurred and the smaller drains at shallower depths. An alternative is to use inclined auger-bored drains.

2.10 ARTIFICIAL SEAWEED

Model tests at the Hydraulics Research Station, Wallingford, have shown that artificial seaweed placed off-shore transferred shorewards some sand from off-shore. Observations established that the effect of the artificial seaweed is to increase the net drift near the bed towards the shore.

Field trials were carried out at Bournemouth. 'Pony-tails' of artificial seaweed (polypropylene), each containing 1 lb (0·45 kg) of synthetic fibre (specific gravity 0·95), 8 ft (2·4 m) long, attached to a 6 lb (2·7 kg) weight, were spaced at 1 yd (1 m) intervals to form a grid 400 ft (122 m) long by 150 ft (46 m) wide. The lines of the grid, 150 ft (46 m) long were held in position by a 1 cwt (51 kg) anchor at each end.

Surveys indicated that a small build-up of sand was taking place shorewards of the seaweed. However, subsequent examination showed that the seaweed had been severely damaged by storms, so that the results were inconclusive.

Much more fieldwork is necessary—it has still to be established that (a) it is possible to make and anchor artificial seaweed so that it will not be damaged by storms, (b) that the seaweed will create sufficient accretion to make its use practicable for coast protection, and (c) that the cost of providing and installing the seaweed is acceptable·in the light of what it achieves.

2.11 EXPERIMENTAL GRASS SOWING ON SAND DUNES

After a number of experiments the most successful method was found to be the 'discing in' of chopped straw to a surface prepared by bulldozing, sowing the grass seed and applying a second straw mulch to give added protection. Autumn sowings carried out in this way have proved successful in establishing a good grass cover through the straw which prevents sand blowing during early germination. A high nitrogen content fertiliser, specially prepared to remain effective over periods of 9–12 months, is applied to provide the necessary nourishment for healthy growth.

The grass seed mixture consists of the following:

  76 lb (34·5 kg) S.143 Cocksfoot B.C.
  21 lb (9·5 kg) Creeping Red Fescue Canadian
   3 lb (1·4 kg) Ribgrass
  12 lb (5·4 kg) Birdsfoot Trefoil

BIBLIOGRAPHY

Beach Formation by Waves: Some Model Experiments in a Wave Tank, R. A. Bagnold, *J. Instn. Civ. Engrs.* Nov. 1940

Sand Movement by Waves: Some Small-scale Experiments with Sand of very low Density, R. A. Bagnold, *J. Instn. Civ. Engrs.*, Feb. 1947

The Influence of a Vertical Wall on a Beach in front of it, R. C. H. Russell and C. C. Inglis, *Proc. Minnesota International Hydraulics Convention,* Sept. 1953

Shore Protection Planning and Design, Beach Erosion Board, Washington, 1954

Hydraulics Research 1956, 1957, 1958, H.M.S.O.

How Beaches are supplied with Shingle, J. A. Steers, *Proc. Sixth International Conference on Coastal Engineering,* 1957, University of Florida, pub. by the U.S. Council on Wave Research, University of California

The Formation of Artificial Sand Dunes as a Means of Coastal Protection, J. Tuora, *Civil Engineering,* Feb. 1956

Coast Erosion and Defence, R. C. H. Russell, *Hydraulics Research Paper No. 3,* 1960, H.M.S.O.

Cliff Drainage and Beach Distribution, W. T. Fryde, *Proc. Eleventh International Conference on Coastal Engineering,* 1968, London, pub. by the American Society of Civil Engineers

The Effects of Artificial Seaweed in Promoting the Build-up of Beaches, W. A. Price, K. W. Tomlinson, J. N. Hunt, *Proc. Eleventh International Conference on Coastal Engineering,* 1968, London, pub. by the American Society of Civil Engineers

Chapter 3

Sea Walls, Estuary Walls and Counterwalls

SOIL MECHANICS CONSIDERATIONS

3.1 TYPES OF WALL FAILURE

Clay walls may fail from one or more of the following causes:
(a) direct frontal erosion by wave action,
(b) flow through the fissured zone causing a shallow slump to occur on the landward face of the wall,
(c) scour of the back of the wall by overtopping,
(d) failure by gravitational slip,
(e) delayed slip,
(f) failure of landward side of the wall by uplift pressure acting through permeable underlying strata.

Walls made of sandy permeable material may fail from causes (a) and (c) above and:
(g) as a result of seepage drag forces reducing the stability of the wall,
(h) by local slumping or by local erosion caused by water seeping out above the landward toe of the wall.

3.2 FRONTAL EROSION

Protection from direct frontal attack by wave action can only be given by providing a suitable revetment (see Chapter 4).

3.3 THE FISSURED ZONE AND SHALLOW SLUMPS

A common cause of failure is from flow through the fissured zone. Most clay sea and estuary walls (but not necessarily non-tidal river walls where high water levels may be maintained) have a fissured zone extending to a depth of 1 or 1·25 m below the surface caused by the drying out of the surface and reduction of moisture content resulting from vegetational growth.

At times of exceptional high tide, water flows through the fissures and shallow slumps may result, as illustrated by *Figure 34*.

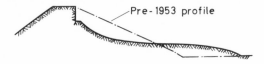

Figure 34. Shallow slip failure at Motney Hill—Medway Estuary

If the top width of the wall is narrow the effect of the slump will often be to reduce the height, width and strength of that part of the wall to such an extent that a breach and complete failure follows.

Safeguards against this type of failure are: (a) to raise the walls at least 1 m above the highest known tide, this applies particularly to estuary walls, (b) to make the back slope equal to or flatter than $2\frac{1}{2}$: 1, (c) to make the top of the wall sufficiently wide so that breaching will not necessarily follow a shallow slip occurring on the landward slope, (d) to lay a 75 mm layer of ashes along the top of the wall; this helps to prevent loss of moisture and, thus, to reduce fissuring.

3.4 BACK SCOUR

Scouring of the back of the wall, if it is too severe for turf to provide sufficient protection, can generally only be combated by constructing a protective revetment (see Chapter 4).

In some areas tipping of suitable waste materials behind the wall can be an effective means of strengthening the wall and preventing at little cost the possibility of breaches occurring.

3.5 ROTATIONAL SLIP—SLIP CIRCLE ANALYSIS

Failure by rotational slip is a common cause of wall failure during the carrying out of heightening works, and *Figure 35* shows the mechanism of a slip of this kind. Such a slip occurred on the landward side of the wall at Scrapsgate. *Figure 36* shows the heave in the delph ditch that followed, and *Figure 37* shows the wall profile before and after failure. It is therefore essential that scheme

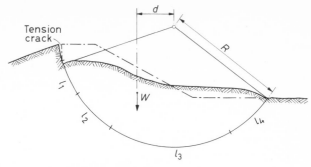

Figure 35. Diagram showing rotational slip

Figure 36. Scrapsgate—heave in bed of delph ditch following failure

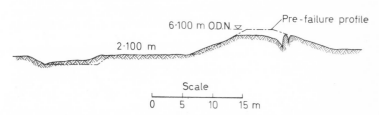

Figure 37. Failure by rotational slip at Scrapsgate—Isle of Sheppey

investigations should include stability analyses to ensure that the proposed improved section will not fail in this way.

Slip circle analysis is frequently employed. Referring to *Figure 35,* and considering a unit run of wall, the factor of safety is

$$\frac{R\Sigma ls}{Wd}$$

A number of trial circles of different radii and centres are taken to determine the arc of least stability. The shear strengths at the various depths are found from samples tested in an unconfined compression test machine, the shear strengths of soft clays being approximately equal to half the compression strengths determined directly by the machine. The method assumes that the shear strengths at the various depths will not decrease after construction. The depth of the tension crack is taken as $2 s/\alpha$, where α is the density of the bank material.

For walls protecting ordinary agricultural land a factor of safety of 1·2 will normally be found adequate. If at one or two sections along the wall the factor of safety is somewhat low it is usually better to proceed with the work, since if a failure occurs during construction it is not a difficult matter to remedy the failure and strengthen the section. This procedure is generally justified since walls normally strengthen with time (but not always and this aspect of design is dealt with later).

For walls protecting built-up areas or valuable industrial property a factor of safety of at least 1·5 is recommended.

In many areas it is found that the saltings in front of a wall are at a higher level than the land protected. In these cases failure by rotational slip landwards on heightening the wall could occur, particularly if there is a delph ditch close to the wall on the landward side. If the factor of safety determined is too low conditions can usually be improved by filling in the ditch and constructing a berm on the landward side. Similarly, where failure is likely on the riverward side the factor of safety can be improved by weighting the riverward toe of the wall. As an alternative to this, if circumstances allow, the wall can be thickened on the landward side, and when the slip has occurred on the seaward side that side can be trimmed and shaped to its flatter stable slope.

As an initial approximation and assuming the shear strength s to be constant at all depths, the maximum height of wall possible with normal side slopes is

$$\frac{5 \cdot 5s}{\alpha}$$

where α is the density of the bank material[1]. Since the shear strength of marsh clays is often about 1·0–1·5 Mg/m² and α about 1·6 Mg/m³, it follows that the height of walls is limited to between 3·5 and 5·20 m above marsh level, unless special (and expensive) works such as berms are provided to increase the factor of safety. The critical wall heights for various clay densities and shear strengths may be read directly from Design Chart G.

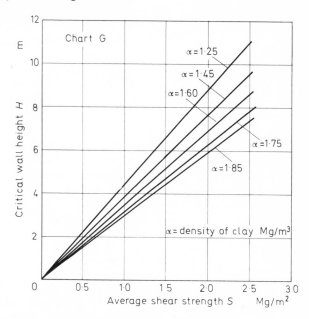

Critical wall heights corresponding to various clay densities and shear strengths

3.6 GRAVITATIONAL SLIP—WEDGE ANALYSIS

Where the underlying strata are thin layers of soft clay, wedge analysis is preferable to slip circle analysis, but the latter method is more accurate for fairly uniform clay deposits. In the former case the surface of sliding consists of several sections which do not run smoothly together so that an error is introduced if the surface is assumed to be an arc of a circle.

Wedge analyses are carried out as follows: referring to *Figure 38*, if P_a is the active disturbing earth force acting on CD, P_p the passive resisting earth force acting on AB and L_2T_2 the shear force acting on BC, then the factor of safety is

$$\frac{P_p + L_2 T_2}{P_a}$$

Trial positions for B and C are taken and wedge analyses carried out until the surface of least factor of safety is determined.

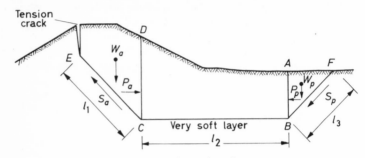

Figure 38. Wedge analysis diagram

For soft clays, CE and FB may be taken as at $45°$ to the horizontal. With a factor of safety of F, if a force diagram is drawn for DCE it will be seen that

$$P_a = W_a - \sqrt{2} S_a = W_a - \frac{\sqrt{2L_1 T_1}}{F}$$

and similarly

$$P_p = W_p + \sqrt{2} S_p = W_p + \frac{\sqrt{2L_3 T_3}}{F}$$

Whence for equilibrium,

$$W_a - \frac{\sqrt{2L_1 T_1}}{F} = W_p + \frac{\sqrt{2L_3 T_3}}{F} + \frac{T_2 L_2}{F}$$

The authors are indebted to Mr. A. Marsland, M.Sc., for this derivation.

3.7 SHEARING RESISTANCE, COHESION, EFFECTIVE AND NEUTRAL STRESSES AND ANGLE OF INTERNAL FRICTION

The general relation between shearing resistance (s), cohesion (c), effective (intergranular) stress (p_1) and the angle of internal friction (ϕ) of soils is given by the equation, $s = c + p_1 . \tan \phi$.

If the load on the soil at a given level is p per unit area and the pore-water pressure (neutral pressure) is u, then $p_1 = p - u$. Thus it will be seen that as the pore pressure increases the shear strength decreases. For clayey soils the pore pressure is usually at a maximum directly after construction and becomes a minimum as the clay consolidates with time. Pore-water pressures vary with change in the imposed shear stress on clays. If it is assumed that the pore-water pressures developed during shearing are the same in both the test and in the ground, then the shear strength results of unconfined compression tests can be taken as the shear strengths of the clay in the stability analyses. Investigations on this assumption are known as $\phi = 0$ analyses. Analyses on this basis for the design of most walls built in marsh areas are used because experience shows them to give satisfactory results with the factors of safety quoted above and because of the ease of carrying out unconfined compression tests.

Values of c and ϕ may be ascertained from samples tested in a triaxial compression machine. The difficulty in attempting to use this information in analysis is to know what value of pore-water pressure to assume.

3.8 DELAYED SLIPS

Delayed slips sometimes occur up to nine months or more after construction. The reasons for these occurring are usually complex and in many cases not fully understood. Among the causes listed by Marsland[1, 2] are re-distribution of pore-water pressure, excessive pore-water pressures resulting from changes in tidal level, banks built of appreciably stiffer material than the very compressive underlying soil, resulting in differential settlement sufficient to cause extensive cracks to develop especially in the centre of the bank.

Even where failure does not occur, slow settlement of walls is very common where the underlying material is very soft.

3.9 STABILITY OF SILT AND SAND WALLS—SWEDISH METHOD OF SLICES

Permeable silt and sand soils are not usually employed in England in the construction of sea walls but they are sometimes used for the construction of counterwalls as second lines of defence some distance landward of the main defences where, if breaches occurred in the main walls, the counterwalls would contain the water flowing through the breaches but would not be subjected to wave action.

The strength of these pervious walls deteriorates as the water level rises towards the crest because of the drag exerted by the seeping water.

Stability analyses for this type of wall are usually based on the Swedish method of slices. The flow net is plotted (by a method described in detail further on) and unit thickness of the wall section is divided into vertical slices above the trial slip circle arc. The total weight of each slice (saturated, if it is below the line of saturation) is resolved at right angles to and tangential to the arc, the former being the normal reaction which, divided by the length of the arc, gives the applied load per unit area p, and the latter the disturbing force F_D.

The average pore-water pressure u acting on the length of arc considered is determined from the flow net and then from the equation given in section 3.7 the shear strength s is obtained. The restoring force F_R is then s times the length of the arc. It therefore follows that the factor of safety is

$$\frac{\Sigma F_R}{\Sigma F_D}$$

In this method the forces between the slices are usually neglected and generally this errs on the side of safety.

Although some scale effects must occur (since using water in the model the Weber number cannot be the same for model and proto-type) it has been shown, for example, by Shukla[3], that reliable information on seepage can be obtained from hydraulic models of permeable walls provided certain simple rules are followed. Where the permeability of the materials in different zones of the embankment differs corresponding portions of the model are made of materials which have the same relative permeabilities. With material coarser than 2 mm the flow is not streamlined. Bearing in mind these conditions a model is made and from it the line of saturation is determined. Once this is known the flow net can be easily plotted by the well known Forchheimer method[2].

3.10 UNDER-DRAINAGE AND FILTERS

If the flow lines reach the surface of the back slope of the wall local failure can occur either in the form of local slumping or local erosion caused by the seeping water carrying the material down the slope. This can be remedied by thickening the bank or by providing an under-drain filter under the landward toe of the wall to 'draw down' the flow.

To be effective the particles forming the filter must not be too small since they must be big enough to provide the drain with a greater permeability than the wall to achieve the required 'draw down'. On the other hand, they must not be too big otherwise the material of the bank could be drawn into the interstices and thus obstruct the flow. These two conditions can be avoided if the Terzaghi criteria are applied that the 15 per cent size (D_{15}) of the filter (*i.e.* size of sieve through which 15 per cent of the sample passes) is at least four times as large as the D_{15} size of the coarsest wall material sample and not more than four times as large as the 85 per cent size (D_{85}) of the finest wall material sample.

In Holland, where sand is much used in sea wall construction, the practice is to provide cut-off walls and an impermeable covering, such as asphalt, on the seaward side and sometimes clay on the landward side, together with adequate under-drainage.

3.11 UPLIFT PRESSURES

If a permeable stratum exists under a clay wall it will be evident that, on high tides, uplift pressures could develop under the wall. These can reduce the stability of the wall by lessening the shear strength of the soil and even by causing the landward toe to heave. Suitable remedies are to provide more weight on the landward side and to provide relief filter drains near the landward toe to reduce the uplift pressures.

GENERAL CONSIDERATIONS

3.12 WAVERLEY COMMITTEE

As a result of the east coast flooding in 1953 a Departmental Committee, known as the Waverley Committee[4] after its chairman, was set up to examine the causes of the flooding and to make such recommendations as they thought necessary. Their main recommendations as far as the design of sea defences is concerned are dealt with in the following paragraphs.

3.13 STANDARD OF PROTECTION

The Committee recommended that where residential and industrial areas or large areas of valuable agricultural land would be affected the standard of protection should be sufficient to withstand the conditions occurring on 31 Jan./1 Feb., 1953.

Elsewhere the standard should be that which would have been thought adequate to withstand the worst known conditions prior to 1953.

In some circumstances, where property of exceptional value has to be protected, or for other exceptional reasons, higher standards than the foregoing could be applied and similarly where the value of the area to be protected is considerably below the general average, lower standards might be appropriate. These recommendations were made in conjunction with their proposal that a flood warning system should be organised. This was done and the system now exists as the Storm Tide Warning Service.

As an example of a higher standard, the Kent River Authority has recently decided that for one densely populated area where evacuation would pose very difficult problems the appropriate standard of protection is that suggested by the Chief Engineer of the Ministry of Agriculture, the 'Johnson' standard, namely that the defences should withstand the 200–300 year conditions without material flooding, and a thousand year tide without disastrous flooding, these criteria being related to conditions 50 years hence.

3.14 COUNTERWALLS AND CROSSWALLS

In many marsh areas counterwalls inland of the main sea defences exist which centuries ago were built as the main sea walls. Crosswalls also often exist between the first and second defence lines dividing the area liable to flooding into 'boxed' compartments.

The Waverley Committee recommended that these secondary defences, where serving a useful purpose, should be maintained, and if necessary improved, and that consideration should be given to the construction of new second-line defences where the potential benefit would justify the cost.

3.15 ACCESS

The Committee stressed the importance of providing easy access to sea defences at times of flooding and pointed out that if access along the top of a wall or along a berm on the landward side were provided, the strength of the wall would be increased. Thus it is that usually the necessary strengthening of a wall can be combined with the provision of access. Crosswalls and counterwalls referred to in section 3.14 may also be adapted to provide access at a high level across the marshes to the main sea walls.

3.16 OUTFALLS AND EVACUATION OF FLOOD WATER

The Committee drew attention to the need in many areas to provide outfalls to ensure the rapid evacuation of flood water. Such outfalls should often be much larger than necessitated by purely land-water drainage requirements. This recommendation applies particularly to built-up and industrial areas where evacuation of flood water in three days or so would enable rehabilitation and resumption of production to be effected quickly.

3.17 SEALING OFF TIDAL CREEKS

The Committee recommended that where there was no conflict with navigation or similar interests consideration should be given to sealing off tidal creeks in order to obviate the need to maintain long lengths of creek walls.

WALL MATERIALS AND CONSTRUCTION

3.18 WALL MATERIALS

Clay is the usual material for wall construction. In parts of Kent where there are difficulties in obtaining a good supply of clay the seaward portions of the walls have been made of clay and the landward portions of more easily obtainable material such as a mixture of chalk and clinker.

In the past the clay for walls has been taken mainly from adjoining delph ditches or borrow pits. Such material has usually a low shear strength and its high moisture content often results in excessive shrinkage occurring. Hand placing permitted much moister clay to be used than is possible with bulldozers. Consequently the current practice is to reduce the moisture content of marsh clay before placing it in the wall, or, alternatively, to use clay taken from hillside borrow pits which will be found usually to have more nearly the correct moisture content for compaction and can therefore often be placed straight into the wall. This imported clay is generally much stronger in shear strength and is also often found to contain a proportion of sand which keeps shrinkage to a minimum.

Heavily pre-compressed (geologically) clays should be avoided, otherwise excessive expansion may cause bad fissuring.

The object of good earthwork embankment construction is to achieve maximum density by packing together the soil particles and expelling the air. Good compaction is ensured if the water content is slightly greater than the plastic limit. If the moisture content is lower voids remain in the wall, and if it is much higher it is impossible to use normal mechanical compaction methods. As a rough guide it may be said that if the material is suitable for satisfactory movement and compaction by bulldozer it has the correct moisture content for placing in the wall.

3.19 CONSTRUCTION

Bulldozing is a very satisfactory method of placing and consolidating clay in sea and river walls, but it is not practicable by this means to build a wall with side slopes much steeper than 2:1 (horizontal to vertical).

Imported clays can often be placed straight into the wall but the moisture content of marsh clay must be reduced before it is placed. The material excavated should be spread for drying to a depth not exceeding 1 m and excavation and spreading should proceed in layers with the lowest and wettest material being placed on top. Top soil and turf need not be laid aside and may be incorporated in the heap.

This work can proceed throughout the year. During the summer period (May to October) when the material has dried sufficiently it can be placed in its initial position in the wall, being taken from the heap by side-cut so that the layers are thoroughly mixed as they are moved. As filling in an improvement scheme proceeds the existing wall should be lightly benched by side-cut with bulldozers in a series of steps as the fill is raised.

The initial placing should be at a gentle slope of, say, 4:1, forming a rough profile behind the existing wall. The following year it should be scarified to a depth of 0·5–1 m, recompacted and shaped to its final profile. Where the improvement is to the back of an existing wall, the landward edge of the crest should, in general, be left at least 150 mm higher than the designed level with a crossfall to seaward to allow for settlement. (The design of landward and seaward aprons on newly placed clay should similarly allow for settlement.) Finally the top 150 mm of the surface can be brought to tilth, grass seed sown and rolled.

When sub-soil conditions are poor and a firm stratum exists only at very great depth, considerable settlement must be expected and allowed for. Some of the Thames tidal river walls in Kent are sinking at rates varying according to site from 25 mm to 75 mm per annum. In such cases it is advisable to make the top of the wall 4·5 m to 6·0 m wide. The wall can then be 'topped up' every few years. When its top width has been reduced by this to about 3·0 m (minimum width for access along the top) major re-profiling works can be carried out at intervals of 10 to 30 years.

REFERENCES

1. The Design and Construction of Earthen Flood Banks, A. Marsland, *J. Inst. W.E.* vol. 11, No. 3, May, 1957
2. *River Engineering and Water Conservation Works,* Ed. R. B. Thorn, Butterworths, London, 1966
3. Importance of Model Studies in the Design of Earth Dams, K. P. Shukla, *Symposium on Role of Models in the Evolution of Hydraulic Structures and Movement of Sediment—1952,* Publication No. 53, Central Board of Irrigation and Power, India (publ. 1954)
4. *Report of the Department Committee on Coastal Flooding,* H.M.S.O., 1954
5. *Soil Mechanics in Engineering Practice,* K. Terzaghi and R. B. Peck, Wiley, London, 1948

Chapter 4

The Hydraulic Design of Sea Wall Profiles, and Revetment Details

4.1 GENERAL CONSIDERATIONS

Reliable knowledge is of the greatest value in the design of sea defence works and before any proposals are put forward as much information as possible should be collected of previous foreshore conditions, the effects of storms, littoral drift, dominant winds, currents, heights and period of waves, foreshore formation and materials and of all other factors that influence conditions where the works are to be constructed.

Estuarial flood embankments are usually protected against severe wave action by the estuary itself and by the saltings which are often at a higher level than the land protected by the wall. Rice grass is widely used to resist erosion and assist accretion of the saltings (see section 2.8).

The top of a clay wall should preferably be at least 1 m above highest known tide level so that the risk of water flowing through the surface fissures is reduced to a minimum, and correspondingly higher if appreciable wave action is anticipated.

Soil mechanics, standards of protection and similar considerations are dealt with in Chapter 3 and this chapter is concerned mainly with profile and revetment design from hydraulic and structural considerations. If the soil is such that the desirable level for the top of the wall cannot be attained without rotational slip occurring then two alternatives are possible. The first is to construct a crest wall (details of different designs of this type are given in Chapter 5) and the second (sometimes combined with the first) is to provide adequate protection to the back of the wall so that it may be overtopped without damage at high tide during severe storms. In most cases the period of overtopping is short, occurring only at the peak of the tide, and the quantity of water passing over the wall is often comparatively small so that it can easily be absorbed by the marsh dyke

68

system and discharged to the sea through gravity outfalls as the tide falls.

A common batter for the front and rear of earthen estuarial walls is 3:1 (horizontal to vertical); 2:1 is about the practical limit if modern means of construction by bulldozer are used and flatter slopes have often to be employed on the seaward face, particularly on exposed lengths and on the landward face, if overtopping is expected, where no special protection other than good turf is provided. These aspects are dealt with in greater detail further on in this chapter and also in Chapter 3.

Protection against attrition by wave action caused by wind or by wash from navigation may take the form of brushwood faggots which also assist accretion of silt, of dumped or pitched stone, of sheet piling or of concrete blocks. Usually an essential requirement of all forms of revetment for river and sea walls is flexibility, since slow settlement of one or other of the types described in Chapter 3 occurs on many of these walls.

On the larger sea walls the blockwork is usually contained in panels so that if a wash-out occurs the spread of the damage is limited. On the foreshore the panel walls often consist of timber or steel sheet piling and a toe wall of sheet piling is frequently used, but on the main part of the seaward face where settlement may be expected and where tide levels do not present great constructional difficulties the panels are usually of reinforced concrete with hinge joints to ensure flexibility.

4.2 TYPES OF SEA WALL

The 18th International Congress on Navigation in Rome in 1953 divided sea walls into two main classes, those from which waves are reflected and those on which waves break. It was generally agreed that any intermediate type that gives a combination of reflection and breaking sets up very severe erosive action of the sea bed in front of the wall. A slope of about 2:1 is the steepest on which waves will break.

The second category can be sub-divided into two main groups, (a) those where the depth of water in front of the wall is such that waves break on the structure, and (b) those where the bigger waves break on the foreshore in front of the wall.

The Northern sea wall and the Dymchurch sea wall are examples of type (a) (*Figures 39* to *46*) and the Seasalter sea wall (*Figures 47* and *48*) is an example of type (b).

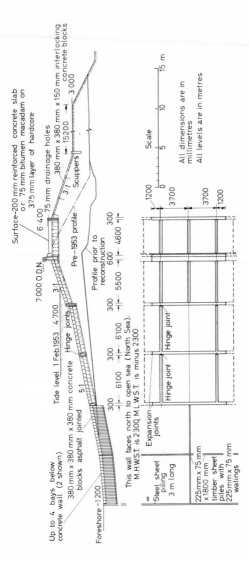

Surface–200 mm reinforced concrete slab
or 75 mm bitumen macadam on
375 mm layer of hardcore

380 mm x 380 mm x 150 mm interlocking
concrete blocks

75 mm drainage holes

3·000

15200

3·1

Scuppers

6·400

7·000 O.D.N.

Pre-1953 profile

Profile prior to
reconstruction

300   600   300

5500   4600

300   6100   300   6100   300

Tide level 1 Feb.1953   4·700   3·1

Hinge joints

380 mm x 380 mm concrete
blocks asphalt jointed   5:1

Up to 4 bays below
concrete wall (2 shown)

Foreshore –1·200

This wall faces north to open sea (North Sea).
M.H.W.S.T. is 2300, M.L.W.S.T. is minus 2300

Expansion
joints

Hinge joint   Hinge joint

Hinge joint

Steel sheet
piling
3 m long

225mm x 75 mm
x1800 mm
timber sheet
piles with
225 mm x 75 mm
walings

1200

3700

3700

1200

Scale

0   5   10   15 m

All dimensions are in
millimetres
All levels are in metres

Figure 39. Details of Northern sea wall type V

Figure 40. Northern sea wall type V under construction

Figure 41. Northern sea wall type V, seaward face, showing 15 in (380 mm) (cube) concrete blocks set in asphalt jointing

Figure 42. Northern sea wall type V—seaward face and top (before laying of roadway surface)

Figure 43. Northern sea wall type V, roadway and landward slope (showing interlocking blocks)

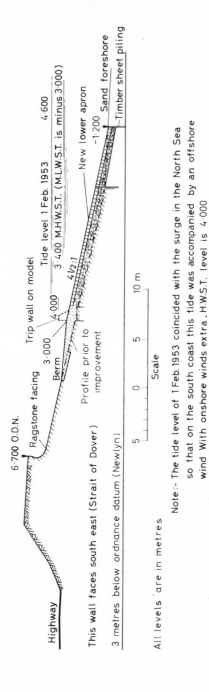

6·700 O.D.N.

Ragstone facing

Trip wall on model

Berm

3·000

Tide level 1 Feb. 1953   4·600

3·400 M.H.W.S.T. (M.L.W.S.T. is minus 3·000)

4·000

4½:1

Profile prior to improvement

New lower apron

−1·200

Sand foreshore

Timber sheet piling

Highway

This wall faces south east (Strait of Dover)

3 metres below ordnance datum (Newlyn)

Scale

5   0   5   10 m

All levels are in metres

Note:- The tide level of 1 Feb. 1953 coincided with the surge in the North Sea so that on the south coast this tide was accompanied by an offshore wind With onshore winds extra. H.W.S.T. level is 4·000

Figure 44. Dymchurch sea wall profile, Grand Redoubt to Willop

Figure 45. Dymchurch sea wall, view from Grand Redoubt to Willop

Figure 46. Dymchurch sea wall, south of Willop, view looking north

Figure 47. Seasalter sea wall

4.3 APRON SLOPES AND BERMS

The general effect of flattening the slope is to lessen the swash height, lessen foreshore erosion and reduce the wave pressure on the upper part of the apron. It therefore follows that the smaller the depth of water in front of the wall at high tide (and hence the smaller the waves that can approach it) and the more inerodible the foreshore, the steeper may the revetment be. The slope may therefore vary from 2:1 (horizontal to vertical) for an estuary wall well protected by a wide clay salting at a high level and by the estuary (the 2:1 slope also being about the practical limit from

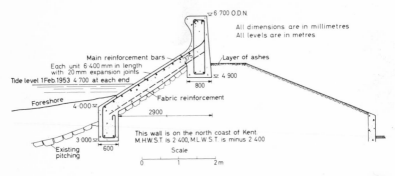

Figure 48. Details of Seasalter sea wall

earthwork constructional considerations) to 5:1 or even flatter for a sea wall in deep water that permits large waves to approach and break on the wall.

In the past, elliptical (or parabolic) profiles have been popular and the Dymchurch sea wall, south of Willop (*Figure 46*), is an example of a wall of this type. Frequently, however, in the cases of the higher walls this has been considered to entail an excessive parabolic development and the lower part of the apron has been of uniform slope. The considerations to be taken into account in deciding seaward revetment profiles are set out below. The golden rule should be, if in doubt or disagreement as to the best profile to adopt, do not be dogmatic but carry out model tests on the various alternatives and from the results determine the most suitable design.

The sea walls at Dymchurch in Kent provide interesting informa-
tion on apron slopes since with their varying profiles they can be regarded as full-scale models tested over the years by the worst combinations of conditions. On the length from Grand Redoubt to Willop, *Figures 44* and *45*, the apron was made steeper many

years ago and to a slope of $4\frac{1}{2}$:1. At highest recorded tide level there was nearly 6 m of water in front of the wall. The wall has suffered considerable damage by wave action and the sand fore-shore in front of it has dropped to the lowest level for this part of the coast, whereas the wall adjoining it immediately south of Willop (*Figure 46*), which is elliptical in profile and of similar construction but of flatter slope (average slope of main part of apron $7\frac{1}{2}$:1), has no history of damage and maintains a much higher foreshore level in front of it (the foreshore level changes rapidly over a short length at the change in apron section). This latter point stresses the need for flat slopes to limit disturbance of the natural foreshores (particularly those of sand) to a minimum. Undoubtedly the steeper the slope the greater the wave reflection and hence the greater the turbulence in front of the wall, which creates a lower sand level by putting more sand in suspension which is carried by the tidal currents and deposited on adjoining lengths where the slope of the apron is flatter and the turbulence less. The effect of impermeable structures on foreshore stability is discussed in section 2.3.

Present-day knowledge of this aspect of design is unsatisfactory and research is needed to determine the effects of different apron slopes on sand foreshores.

Modern practice is to put a berm on the seaward side of the wall at about the level of high water; the effect of this in reducing swash height will be seen from the swash height expression given in section 1.10, and from Design Charts D and E, page 12. For maxi-mum effectiveness it is found that the berm width must be about one-fifth of the wave length. Tests on the Northern sea wall model, see *Figure 49*, showed that when an 11 m wide berm was added no great improvement was observed for waves of 10 sec period but that conditions were materially improved for waves of

Figure 49. Northern sea wall model under test

6 and 8 sec period. Wave heights taken in the tests ranged from 1 to 4·2 m.

The expression given in Chapter 1 applies to berms at high water level. Little information is available about the effect of berms at lower levels although it will be obvious that such berms would be much cheaper to construct. On the front of one length of wall at All Hallows in North Kent a berm was built of width approximately one-quarter the wave length and at a level below high water approximately equal to the wave height. Experience has shown this to be very effective in reducing wave action on the pitching, this length remaining undamaged at times when quite extensive damage has occurred to the pitching on the lengths on either side of it. Thorndike Saville's method (pages 11 and 17) may be used with advantage in studies of the possible behaviour of profiles of this type.

Figure 44 shows the recent improvement to the Dymchurch sea wall on the length from Grand Redoubt to Willop referred to above. Model tests showed that the berm was most effective in reducing wave action on the upper part of the apron and in assisting the reduction of water passing over the wall. Tests on alternative profiles showed this one to be most satisfactory and its adoption served a fourfold purpose: strengthening of the lower apron that had been weakened by severe abrasion, reduction in wave action on the upper part of the apron thereby removing the need to carry out expensive strengthening works on that part, reduction of overtopping thus reducing the risk of damage to the unprotected landward face of the wall, and provision of an access berm for plant for groyne and wall maintenance, of great value since the distance from wave wall to toe is too great for the reach of normal cranes. The waves reproduced in the tests were of 6, 7, 8, and 9 sec periods and of heights varying from 0·7 to 3·9 m.

Above the berm or above high water it is frequently the practice to steepen the slope, and slopes of 3:1 for (a) type walls and 2:1 for (b) type walls are common for this upper portion.

4.4 STEPWORK, WAVE WALLS, TRIP WALLS AND ROUGHNESS BLOCKS

Figure 49 shows the model of the Northern sea wall under test and under the worst conditions reproduced in the test the ineffectiveness of stepwork and curved wave wall will be seen. For this reason plain blockwork was used in place of the stepwork on the actual structure. Another objection to stepwork is that the arrises become quickly abraded if the foreshore is of shingle.

Curved wave walls however are more effective under less severe conditions in throwing swash seawards and as these less severe conditions are the more usual it is generally felt that such wave walls serve a useful purpose. Again for less exposed sea walls on sandy foreshores where abrasion is not severe stepwork is more durable and has the merit of reducing swash height and scour at the toe of the wall under some less severe conditions.

A trip wall (shown in broken line on *Figure 44*) was added to the Dymchurch sea wall model to ascertain its effect and it was found that at extra high tide all waves both large and small broke with considerable impact on the trip wall sending spray in all directions, a great deal of which would on the prototype be carried over the wall by the onshore wind to damage the landward face of the wall.

Roughness blocks in the form of cylinders 1·2 m in diameter with 1·2 m spaces between them were also tried but again these greatly increased the amount of spray thrown into the air and were therefore considered undesirable, quite apart from their obvious shortcomings from amenity and aesthetic aspects.

As distinct from large roughness blocks, aprons with rough surfaces, e.g. roughly laid stone, have the advantage that they can reduce the swash height up to about 15 per cent.

4.5 EFFECT OF WAVE ACTION ON BLOCKWORK

The seaward face of the Dymchurch sea wall model (*Figure 44*) was made of rigid materials except for one line of loosely held blocks 11 mm square and 13 mm deep, approximately equivalent to 300 mm cubes in the prototype. They sat in cubical holes 13 mm square and 13 mm deep, and the movement of the blocks was regarded as a measure of the wave attack. Waves greater than 0·7 m in height removed cubes at the point where the waves plunged, while waves 0·7 m high removed one cube. The number of cubes removed was taken as a measure of the wave attack.

The ease with which waves of small height removed 300 mm cubes showed that the strength of the apron did not lie so much in the weight of the individual stones as in the water-tightness and strength of the mortar joining the stones.

To investigate this further, tests were carried out on a panel representing 380 mm × 380 mm × 200 mm interlocking blocks of the Kent River Authority type (described in section 4.9). The linear scale was 1 in 24 and the density scale 1 : 1. Prototype waves of 7 sec period were reproduced. Waves of small height were first generated with the level of still-water low and the water level was then slowly raised until the waves were breaking well above the panel of blocks. If no blocks were removed the wave height was increased and the experiment was repeated until a block was pulled out. It was observed that quite small waves disturbed individual blocks or small areas of the panel without removing them, and after each disturbance they fell back again into position.

It was found that the resistance of the blocks to movement was dependent on the tightness with which they fitted into the panel.

When there was no clearance between the blocks no wave that could be reproduced (up to a maximum of 2·8 m in height) pulled blocks out. When the total clearance between all the blocks in a row (of 8 or 9 blocks per row) was 0·3 or 6 mm in prototype dimensions the smallest wave that pulled blocks out was found to be either 1·8 m high or 1·4 m high depending on the conditions round the edge of the panel. Greater clearance between the blocks resulted in poorer resistance to wave attack. The alternative conditions round the edge of the panel represented, firstly, concrete effectively bonding the peripheral blocks to the frame and, secondly, concrete not bonding these blocks to the frame and allowing movement, that is the outside edges of the blocks forming the perimeter of the panel were filed so that they were free to slide up and down in the frame.

This set of experiments demonstrated the importance of the interlocking, or in the case of plain blocks, of the strength of the mortar joining the blocks, in determining the ability of a revetment to withstand wave action.

4.6 MODELS

Models are of great assistance in the design of sea walls. Since, in deep water, wave velocity is a function of the wave length and, in shallow water, a function of the depth of the water, models are made to natural scales, i.e. geometrically similar to the prototype. There is a limit to the smallness of the models, for if the scale is of the order of 1/150 or less the wave characteristics will probably be affected by friction and surface tension.

In making models and interpreting the results it is essential to grasp clearly the inherent limitations of this approach to design, and the following is a short summary of the basic ideas on which model experimentation is founded.

The principle of dynamical similarity requires that all forces acting on the prototype and model should be in the same ratio. From Newton's second law, force = mass × acceleration, if suffixes

p and m denote prototype and model, respectively, and F_p/F_m, etc., be written F_r, then

$$F_r = M_r \times a_r = \rho_r \times L_r^3 \times \frac{L_r}{T_r^2} = \rho_r \times L_r^2 \times V_r^2 \qquad (4.1)$$

With hydraulic models three basic forces have usually to be considered: gravity, viscosity and surface tension.

If, as for sea walls, the only force acting is gravity, because by ensuring the scale is considerably greater than 1/150 the other forces are kept negligible in comparison, then $F_r = \rho_r \times L_r^3 \times g_r$. Equating this to eqn (4.1) above,

$$\frac{V_r^2}{L_r \times g_r} = 1 \text{ or } \frac{V_p^2}{L_p \times g_p} = \frac{V_m^2}{L_m \times g_m}$$

where $V/(L \times g)^{\frac{1}{2}}$ is the dimensionless Froude number, from which it follows that the Froude number must be the same for model and prototype. V_p/V_m is therefore equal to $[(L_p \times g_p)/(L_m \times g_m)]^{\frac{1}{2}}$.

Sea wall models using water and geometrically similar to the prototype will therefore have the Froude number the same for model and prototype, since V_m/V_p will equal $L_m^{\frac{1}{2}}/L_p^{\frac{1}{2}}$ which equals $(L_m \times g)^{\frac{1}{2}}/(L_p \times g)^{\frac{1}{2}}$ or, $V_m/(L_m \times g)^{\frac{1}{2}} = V_p/(L_p \times g)^{\frac{1}{2}}$, i.e. the Froude number for the model is equal to that of the prototype.

Hence, if the linear scale L_m/L_p is $1/S$, the velocity scale V_m/V_p is $1/S^{\frac{1}{2}}$, the discharge scale (for overtopping tests as described below) Q_m/Q_p is equal to $1/S^{\frac{5}{2}}$ and the time scale is $1/S^{\frac{1}{2}}$.

Preliminary wall profiles should be designed in accordance with the general principles set out in this chapter. Alternative designs can then be tested by models to determine the most suitable. Alternative designs investigated can, for example, include trial wave walls of different shapes. Descriptions of some wall profile model tests are given in sections 4.3 and 4.4.

It is sometimes necessary to find out the likely volume of overtopping that could occur under severe conditions. In such tests it is usual to assume that the overtopping by irregular waves would be similar to that of uniform waves of the same significant height. *Figure 50(a)* and *(b)* shows overtopping tests on a suggested improved profile for a length of the Sheerness sea wall carried out at the Hydraulics Research Station. The model was undistorted and to a scale of 1:20. This gave time and velocity scales of 1:4·46 and a discharge scale of 1:1789 since, as seen above, for geometrically similar models, if the linear scale L_m/L_p is $1/S$ then the time and velocity scales are $1/S^{\frac{1}{2}}$ and the discharge scale $1/S^{\frac{5}{2}}$.

The measure of wave attack on profiles and on areas of blockwork

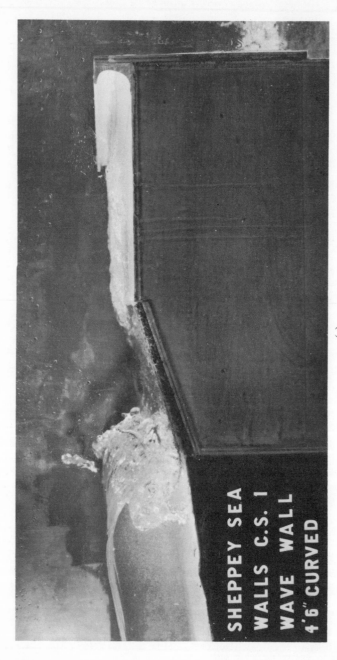

SHEPPEY SEA
WALLS C.S. 1
WAVE WALL
4'6" CURVED

(a)

(b)

Figure 50. Sheerness sea wall model under test
(Reproduced by permission H.M.S.O., courtesy Hydraulics Research Station, Wallingford)

can also be investigated by models, and section 4.5 gives details of some experiments of this kind.

It may be asked what reliance may be placed on the results of tests to determine the stability of ungrouted blocks under wave action. Considering hydraulic and gravitational forces only the following analysis will show that such tests can be expected to give a reasonable indication of conditions likely to occur on the proto-type. It is essential to ensure that the principle of dynamical similarity applies, that is that the disturbing forces are scaled down in the same ratio as the restoring forces. To take a typical case, consider a cube resting on a plane surface and submerged by the swash moving over the surface at velocity V. The cube can be moved either by overturning about the landward bottom edge or by sliding. The overturning force is

$$(\rho_w V^2/g) \times (l^3/2) \tag{4.2}$$

the sliding force is

$$(\rho_w V^2 l^2)/g \tag{4.3}$$

and the corresponding restoring forces are, respectively,

$$(\rho_b - \rho_w)l^4/2 \tag{4.4}$$

and $\qquad\qquad \mu(\rho_b - \rho_w)l^3 \tag{4.5}$

Now, for geometrically similar models of this type, velocity is proportional to the square root of an appropriate linear dimension, so that $V_m^2/V_p^2 = l_m/l_p$;

if the same liquid is used in the model and prototype the ratio of the overturning forces F_m/F_p from eqn (4:2) is l_m^4/l_p^4

and the ratio of the restoring forces from eqn (4.4) is also l_m^4/l_p^4.

Similarly, the ratio of the sliding forces is from eqn (4.3) l_m^3/l_p^3,

and of the restoring forces is also l_m^3/l_p^3,

i.e. dynamical similarity is achieved; that is, the ratios of the disturbing forces in the model and prototype are equal to the ratios of the restoring forces in the model and prototype. Other disturbing forces acting on the blocks are the reduction of pressure on the top and leeward faces, and the drag of the water on the top and sides, but all these are also approximately proportional to the square of the velocity.

It should, however, be noted that whilst model tests will give reasonable results for loose blocks and even for interlocking blocks they cannot give information about grouted blocks because the strength of the grout cannot be simulated.

4.7 STONE PITCHING, KEYED, CEMENT/SAND MORTAR AND ASPHALT GROUTED

Stone pitching is an ancient form of protection to estuary walls and consists of stone (in Kent usually ragstone of nominal thickness 225 mm) properly placed on the clay face of the wall and keyed by wedge-shaped stones firmly driven into place. Revetments of this type are flexible and have proved very satisfactory in the past. They are, in fact, often found superior to flexible concrete blockwork under conditions where excessive local movement of the apron may be expected.

The difficulty at the present time is to find sufficient skilled men capable of carrying out the work. *Figure 51* shows a length of

Figure 51. Keyed ragstone pitching—Upchurch, Medway Estuary

keyed ragstone pitching on a length of wall at Upchurch, on the Medway Estuary.

Alternatives to the skilled process of keying when laying new work are to grout the blocks with asphalt or to brush in a weak cement/sand grout (say 1:8). In the latter case cracks appear if there is settlement which can be easily cut out and regrouted as a part of routine maintenance. Asphalt jointing is particularly suitable when greater settlement and degree of exposure are expected and provides a flexible apron. If it is used the stones, which should be clean, should be primed before grouting with a 50/50 blend of bitumen and white spirit, otherwise the asphalt may tend to come away from the stone. The specification of asphalt for sea defence work is a matter for specialists and expert advice can always be obtained from petroleum companies that supply bitumen. Terms used in asphalt work are defined in section 4.10.

The most suitable composition naturally depends on the climatic temperature, aspect (*i.e.* whether facing north of south, for example), the slope of the pitching and the size of the joints, but as an indication of the proportions likely to be used for this type of work, a suitable compound for use in England on pitching laid at a normal slope would be by weight 47 per cent bitumen of 20/30 penetration,

Figure 52. Asphalt jointed pitching at Ravelin Battery, Sheerness, Isle of Sheppey

47 per cent sand (passing a 10 mesh sieve but retained on a 200 mesh sieve) and 6 per cent asbestos fibres. *Figure 52* shows asphalt jointed pitching at Ravelin Battery, Sheerness, Isle of Sheppey.

For roughly laid stone or slag an asphalt comprising 73 per cent sand, 10 per cent filler (minimum 70 per cent passing 200 mesh sieve) and 17 per cent bitumen of 60/70 penetration would be suitable in many cases and asphalt of this composition was used on the Lincolnshire coast following the 1953 floods.

Suitable stable cold emulsions are sometimes used as an alternative to hot bituminous compounds. They have the advantage that often the sand need not be dried (unless it is very wet) and heating is obviated. An appropriate grout would be 1 litre of suitable proprietary cold emulsion to 0·01 m³ of sand.

It is common also to add Portland cement to the mix; this causes dehydration throughout the mass and the initial set occurs quickly, in under an hour. A suitable mix for jointing packed stone would be by weight of the order 70 per cent sand, 8 per cent cement, 22 per cent bitumen emulsion, but again expert advice is necessary in any particular case and for any specific proprietary cold binder.

4.8 GRANITE BLOCKWORK AND CONCRETE BLOCKWORK

Granite blockwork is one of the finest forms of revetment for resisting severe abrasion. Relative durabilities and relative costs of various types of blockwork are given in section 4.12 from which the value of granite will be evident. It is obviously essential to provide a good mortar and for 300 mm thick blocks the following would be satisfactory: 1 vol. sulphate-resisting cement to $2\frac{1}{2}$ vols. all-in granite aggregate to Table 3 of B.S. 1201, to 2 per cent by weight (of cement) calcium chloride, together with sufficient air entraining agent to provide 3–5 per cent by volume of entrained air (for workability with low water/cement ratio).

Alternatives to granite are other igneous rocks such as basalt.

Figure 53 gives details of 15 in × 15 in × 14 in (380 mm × 380 mm × 355 mm) concrete blocks for use where settlement is not expected. The shape of the joints 'locks' in the jointing mortar. Blocks of this type were used for the reconstruction of the Dymchurch sea wall (*Figure 44*) and were made of gap-graded concrete which tests showed was at least equal to continuously-graded concrete with regard to frost and sulphate resistance, and materially superior with regard to abrasion resistance.

The aggregates for the mix were $1\frac{1}{2}$ in (38 mm) single size shingle and $\frac{3}{16}$ in (4·8 mm) down sand, all to B.S. 882. The mix was, by weight, 78 per cent coarse aggregate, 22 per cent sand, aggregate/cement ratio 5·5. With a water/cement ratio of 0·37, and using rapid-hardening cement, this gave a mean compressive strength at 7 days of 7990 lb/in² (55·1 N/mm²), which corresponds to over 9000 lb/in² (62·1 N/mm²) at 28 days. The required minimum strength at 28 days, using rapid-hardening cement, was 6800 lb/in² (46·9 N/mm²)—the corresponding value for ordinary Portland cement was 6000 lb/in² (41·4 N/mm²). Assuming, with very high control, a value of 83 per cent for the minimum strength as percentage of average strength, an average strength at 28 days of at least

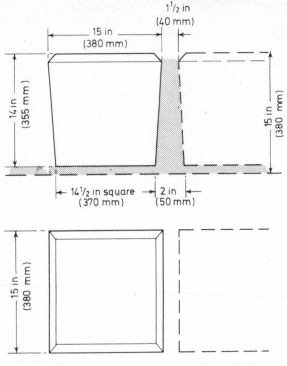

Figure 53. Details of Dymchurch sea wall type blocks

8200 lb/in² (56·5 N/mm²) was needed and therefore this mix was considered satisfactory. Subsequent site tests showed this assumption to be justified.

The mortar for these blocks was as recommended above for granite blockwork but substituting crushed stone or gravel (in quality conforming to the requirements of B.S. 882 but in grading to Table 3 of B.S. 1201) in place of the granite aggregate.

4.9 INTERLOCKING CONCRETE BLOCKS

On walls where wave action is not severe interlocking concrete blocks provide a very satisfactory form of revetment and have the merit that they can be laid rapidly by unskilled labour.

Their chief advantages structurally are: (a) that they are flexible, so that there is no risk of the apron arching over hollows and subsequently failing when exposed to wave attack. Subsidence is quickly noticed as the blocks flex showing up the depressions and if the subsidence is too great the blocks can be quickly lifted and re-laid after the hollows have been filled. (b) As the blocks are not jointed with mortar, hydrostatic pressures building up under the apron are released before any damage is done and where they are used to give protection to the landward side of the wall the apron is not impermeable and there is perhaps therefore less danger of desiccation of the underlying clay.

The blocks are often used on estuary walls and care has to be taken to ensure that they are not damaged by frost action resulting from alternate wetting and freezing. In tests to investigate this, blocks made from different concrete mixes were immersed in boiling water for long periods and subsequently subjected to alternate freezing and de-freezing. The results showed that blocks made of $1:2:4$ concrete disintegrated after this treatment had been repeated a number of times, whereas $1:1\frac{1}{2}:3$ concrete blocks made of well graded aggregate (and therefore denser) showed no deterioration whatsoever after 30 freezings when the experiment was discontinued. Following the tests the mix adopted was: 1 vol. cement to 3 times R vols of fine aggregate to 3 vols of coarse aggregate, R being the ratio of fine to coarse aggregate determined so that the combined aggregate lies within and nearer to the upper boundary of the grading envelope given by percentage finer than: $\frac{3}{4}$ in sieve, 100 per cent; $\frac{3}{8}$ in sieve, 55 to 65 per cent; $\frac{3}{16}$ in sieve, 35 to 42 per cent; B.S. sieve No. 7, 28 to 35 per cent; B.S. sieve No. 14, 21 to 28 per cent; B.S. sieve No. 25, 14 to 21 per cent; B.S. sieve No. 52, 3 to 5 per cent; B.S. sieve No. 100, 0 per cent. The amount of water used is the absolute minimum necessary consistent with workability and the moulds are vibrated minimum 3000 impulses per min. The minimum compressive strength after 28 days for cube tests is required to be 6000 lb/in² (41·4 N/mm²).

The blocks are made in sizes 15 in × 15 in × 8 in (380 mm × 380 mm × 200 mm) thick and 6 in (150 mm) thick, they may be stepped or plain and are laid in courses breaking joint, often on a thin layer of very weak concrete. This blinding obviates the need to trim finely the clay face and provides a good surface on which to work. Details are given in *Figures 54* and *55*. When laid in panels the peripheral blocks are concreted in and where the areas of the panels are extensive or where the blocks are not laid in panels some of the blocks are staked to the underlying clay by lengths of tubular steel driven through and grouted into holes left in the middle of special blocks. The spacing of the stakes depends on the degree of exposure to wave action.

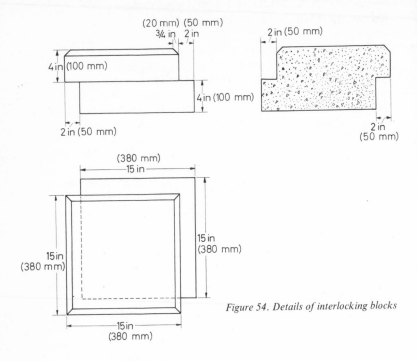

Figure 54. Details of interlocking blocks

Figure 55. Interlocking blocks being laid at Gregory's Point, Isle of Sheppey

4.10 ASPHALT AND ASPHALT PAVING

Asphalt is a mixture of bitumen and inert mineral matter (to avoid confusion it should be noted that bitumen is referred to as asphalt in America), the latter, in sea defence work, usually consisting of one or more of the following: sand (passing 10 mesh sieve but retained on 200 mesh sieve), coarse aggregate, filler (minimum 70 per cent passing 200 mesh sieve), asbestos fibres (used to increase the property of the asphalt to remain in place and not flow on slopes).

Asphalt is flexible, durable, ductile (giving resistance to impact) and resistant to abrasion. If required it can be made impervious and it is not affected chemically by sea water. Within limits the proportions of the different materials can be varied according to the qualities required.

It must be borne in mind, however, that the specific gravity of bitumen is approximately one and in consequence asphalt is very much lighter than concrete. Under water, asphalt has only about 75 per cent of the weight of concrete and therefore wherever it is used care must be taken to prevent the development of hydrostatic pressure under the apron.

The berm of the Pett sea wall (slope 8:1, horizontal to vertical) is an example of the use of asphalt in sea defence work (see *Figures 56* and *57* and Chapter 5) and consists of a two-coat paving laid on shingle. The shingle was sprayed with bituminous emulsion and covered with 25 mm of asphalt, hand-tamped in strips. On this a 50 mm top coat was laid and consolidated by a $2\frac{1}{2}$ ton (2·54 Mg) roller. Because of the shingle foundation the asphalt was made very flexible by the use of high penetration bitumen. Its composition was: base course, 75 per cent sand, 10 per cent limestone filler, 15 per cent bitumen 180/200 penetration; top course, 72 per cent sand, 15 per cent limestone filler, 13 per cent bitumen 180/200 penetration. A drainage system was provided to prevent failure by uplift pressure.

When the foundation is clay care must be taken to clear all growth and spray with weed killer before the asphalt is laid.

If paving is to be used on a wall facing south due regard must be paid to this in deciding the composition of the asphalt, since during the summer months the intensity of the sun's rays on it will be greater than would be the case if it faced north. Only flat slopes would be advisable under such conditions, together with the use of low penetration bitumen. In assessing the possibilities of different types of revetment it should not be forgotten that emergency repairs to asphalt under storm conditions are more difficult than to other types of facings.

All dimensions are in millimetres
All levels are in metres

Pre-cast coping
units 600 mm long

←4700→ ←7500→ ←2400→←1800→←4600→

Asphalt jointed
610 mm x 610 mm x 200 mm
pre-cast concrete blocks

Asphalt jointed
305 mm x 305 mm x 115 mm
pre-cast concrete blocks

7·300 O.D.N.

Two coat
75 mm asphalt   5·500

Tide level 1 Feb. 1953   4·600

Foreshore

225 mm x 350 mm reinforced
concrete coping on
tram rails at 3 m
centres, average
length 6·5 m

3·100

This wall faces S.E.
on the coast of Sussex

←————— 21000 —————→

225 mm x 350 mm reinforced concrete
coping on steel sheet piles
3 m long

Note: The tide level of 1 Feb. 1953 coincided with the surge in the North Sea so that
on the south coast this tide was accompanied by an offshore wind. With onshore
winds extra. H.W.S.T. level is 4·000, M.H.W.S.T. is 3·400, M.L.W.S.T. is minus 3·300.

Scale

|———|———|———|———|———|———|
0   2   4   6   8   10   12 m

Figure 56. Details of Pett sea wall

Figure 57. Pett sea wall

4.11 ASPHALT JOINTED CONCRETE BLOCKS

For estuary walls and for sea walls where wave action is not too great the Essex-type block, *Figure 58*, has been widely used. Those on the top slope of the Pett sea wall (see *Figure 57* and Chapter 5) are 12 in × 12 in × 4½ in (305 mm × 305 mm × 115 mm) thick. The standard Essex River Authority block for estuary walls is 15 in × 15 in × 5 in (380 mm × 380 mm × 125 mm) but where heavier wave action

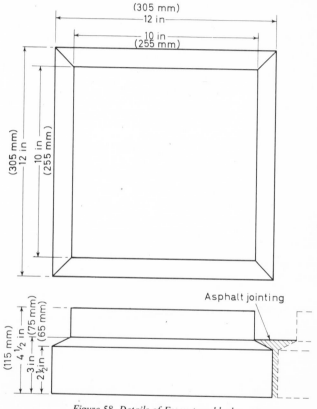

Figure 58. Details of Essex-type blocks

is anticipated, as at Tendring, a 12 in (305 mm) cube is employed. In the foregoing cases the jointing compound formula was 47 per cent bitumen, 47 per cent sand, 6 per cent asbestos fibres. The bitumen penetration varied from 15/25 to 40/50. In comparing blocks of this type with interlocking blocks it should be remembered that if they have to be re-laid it is necessary to clean off the asphalt jointing and that under convex flexing (at the perimeter of a subsided area for example) they are likely to be less strong. A further disadvantage is the difficulty of satisfactory repair work being carried out under bad winter conditions.

For exposure to severe wave action an even heavier block is needed and *Figures 59* and *41* illustrate the 15 in (380 mm) cube blocks used on the Northern sea wall (see Chapter 5). The lower part of the joint is filled with pure bitumen and the upper part with a compound of the proportions by weight, bitumen 47 per cent, sand 47 per cent, asbestos fibres 6 per cent, the sand being $\frac{1}{8}$ in down approved grading, the asbestos 2–4 mm fibres, the bitumen being 20/30 penetration on the 3:1 slope (horizontal to vertical) and 40/50 penetration on the 5:1 slope. The concrete used in the

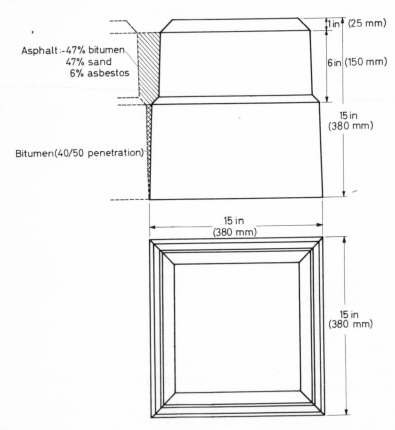

Asphalt:-47% bitumen
47% sand
6% asbestos

1 in (25 mm)

6 in (150 mm)

15 in (380 mm)

Bitumen(40/50 penetration)

15 in (380 mm)

15 in (380 mm)

15 in (380 mm)

Figure 59. Details of Northern sea wall type blocks

blocks is in accordance with the specification given in section 4.9 for interlocking blocks. The sides of the blocks are primed before placing and when necessary the joints are dried by flame gun before the jointing is poured. On the lowest part of the Northern sea wall apron, where settlement could not occur and where it would have been impossible to completely dry the joints, the blocks were grouted in 1:3 cement/sand mortar with, as required, sufficient approved quick-setting additive.

On steep slopes there is a tendency for asphalt jointing to run so that maintenance works are required. In the authors' experience 3:1 should be regarded as the maximum slope desirable.

A possible development in asphaltic jointing material is the addition of rubber to the bitumen (in the proportion of about 5 per cent of the bitumen content) in order to increase the flexibility, and offset any tendency to brittleness. The addition of rubber reduces the penetration of the bitumen so that with it a bitumen one grade lighter should be used.

4.12 RELATIVE DURABILITIES OF VARIOUS FACINGS

There is a regrettable lack of information on the relative durabilities of various types of sea wall facings. In connection with the Dymchurch sea wall reconstruction scheme the following tests were carried out: blocks of granite, concrete and ragstone were, in turn, held stationary in a rotary drum concrete mixer containing shingle, sand and water. The drum was rotated as for mixing concrete. The abrasive material carried to the top of the drum fell on to the surface of the block and rolled down the face, producing an action very similar to natural conditions of sea wall abrasion on shingle and sand foreshores. Each block was kept in the mixer for 10 h. At the end of the tests the surfaces were similar in appearance to those of naturally abraded sea wall facing blocks. The blocks were weighed before and after testing and the percentage loss of weight for each was recorded. The relative durabilities were found to be: granite blockwork, 1; concrete blockwork (to Kent River Authority Specification, age at least 9 months) 0·26; ragstone blockwork, 0·24. The tests were devised and carried out by Mr. J. Evans, B.Sc., C.Eng., F.I.C.E.

The comparative costs for the facings per unit area were: Swedish granite, 1·0; concrete, 0·8; ragstone, 0·68; so that the relative costs per unit area for the life period of the granite were: granite, 1·0; concrete, 2·67; ragstone, 2·85. Ragstone 300 mm thick laid at the seaward toe of the Dymchurch sea wall towards the end of the last century had a useful life of about 50 years so that under the same conditions of sand and shingle abrasion 380 mm granite blocks should last 250 years and 380 mm concrete blocks 68 years.

In situ concrete may be expected to have a shorter life than that of pre-cast blocks since the blocks can: (a) be cast face downwards for added compaction on the face, (b) be cast with a smaller water/cement ratio, giving greater strength, (c) be vibrated better, and (d) are not subject to wave action when setting.

4.13 REINFORCED CONCRETE PANEL WALLS AND WAVE WALLS

On exposed walls the need for constructing blockwork in panels to give, in some cases, greater resistance to wave action and in all cases to limit the area of damage in the event of a wash-out, has already been mentioned. The panel walls are commonly of reinforced concrete.

The upper part of the Northern sea wall revetment (see *Figure 39*) is a typical example of this kind of construction. The box-type units are constructed with expansion joints transversely to accommodate contraction and differential settlement between the adjoining units. To allow for settlement down the slope the units are joined together with hinge joints (for settlement see Chapter 3). The expansion joints are of normal design (that is they are filled with expansion joint material, primed and sealed with sealing compound) and the hinge joints consist of expansion joint material and steel bars or flats wrapped in Densotape or otherwise protected against corrosion, the whole so constructed that a hinge is formed and the revetment given a high degree of flexibility.

The individual units (*i.e.* boxes) forming the panels are designed so that in the event of a wash-out, whatever the means of support of the unit, the stress in the reinforcing steel is below yield point; the amount by which the stress under such conditions is below yield point depending on the degree of likelihood of the unit ever having to be so supported.

Wave walls which usually form part of the upper portion of the panelling are designed with conservative working stresses to withstand the wave pressures exerted on them (see section 1.11) and lateral loads caused by traffic along the crest of the wall.

To ensure satisfactory resistance to sulphate attack, frost action and abrasion, the Kent River Authority specify, for sea walls, vibrated concrete as follows:

Aggregate

Sieve Size	¾ in Aggregate Percentage passing (by weight)	1½ in Aggregate Percentage passing (by weight)
1½ in mesh	100	100
¾ in mesh	100	59–67
⅜ in mesh	55–65	44–52
3/16 in mesh	35–42	32–40
BSS Sieve No. 7	28–35	25–31
BSS Sieve No. 14	21–28	17–24
BSS Sieve No. 25	14–21	12–17
BSS Sieve No. 52	3–5	7–11
BSS Sieve No. 100	0–3	0–2

Mix

Maximum aggregate size 1½ in or ¾ in, limits of aggregate/cement ratio by weight, maximum 5·5, minimum 3·5, minimum crushing strength within 28 days, 6000 lb/in² (41·4 N/mm²).

Cover to bars is at least 50 mm and considerably more where severe abrasion is expected.

4.14 SHEET PILING

Timber and steel sheet piles are used mainly as toe walls to protect sea walls from failure by scour at the toe at times when the foreshore has been lowered by storms and also as panel cut-off walls to contain blockwork at low levels on the foreshore where construction in *in situ* concrete would be unduly difficult and expensive. *Figure 39* illustrates both these uses.

4.15 SUB-APRON GROUTING

It sometimes happens that hollows form under an old sea wall revetment rendering it liable to destruction by heavy wave action. One possible remedy is to pump aerated grout under the apron and this was done with success on the Dymchurch sea wall where hollows had developed between the stonework and the underlying poor quality earthen wall. The equipment comprised a combined mixer and pump, grouting pump and flexible hose.

After experiments the following procedure was adopted. Holes were drilled in the apron at 2 m centres, alternate rows being staggered and 25 mm stand-pipes were caulked into them. Aerated grout in the proportions of 25 kg cement to 76 kg sand to 0·3 litre Teepol and 14 litre water was then pumped through the stand-pipes, commencing on the lower part of the apron and proceeding up the slope. The usual working pressure at the pump was between 1·40 and 1·75 kg/cm^2 and was not allowed to exceed 5·25 kg/cm^2. The sand conformed to the following grading (percentage by weight passing): $\frac{3}{16}$ in. sieve, 100 per cent; B.S. sieve No. 10, 70–100 per cent; B.S. sieve No. 14, 60–100 per cent; B.S. sieve No. 25, 30–100 per cent; B.S. sieve No. 44, 11–72 per cent; B.S. sieve No. 52, 5–64 per cent; B.S. sieve No. 85, 2–40 per cent; B.S. sieve No. 100, 0–14 per cent;

Frequently, water and air were forced up through porous parts of the apron and this was found to be an indication of the path of the grout before it emerged from an adjoining stand-pipe. Rising pressures indicated that ultimate acceptance had been reached. Second and third pressure build-ups were tried in each case and if on the third occasion the pressure went straight up to the maximum the grouting at the particular point was considered complete. The stand-pipe and the adjoining ones from which grout had emerged were then capped.

Samples were taken of the grout emerging from the stand-pipes, from the mixer and from the pump and these showed that the grout retained its aerated form after pumping and after travelling under the apron. After removal of the stand-pipes the holes in the apron were sealed with a cement/sand mix to which Tricosal quick-setting compound had been added.

The average acceptance of aerated grout per hole was 0·14 m^3, the maximum acceptance at a hole was 1·70 m^3 and the average thickness of grout under the apron was 50 mm. Three inspection holes were broken out in the apron. They revealed no voids and at one hole the grout was found to have filled completely what had evidently been a void 100–150 mm in depth and 200–250 mm in width. It had also penetrated well into the lower parts of the block-work joints.

4.16 PERMEABLE SEA WALLS

The tetrapod is an interesting four-legged concrete block developed by the Neyrpic Hydraulic Laboratory. Walls made of these are permeable and the importance of this is discussed in detail in Chapter 2. Their design enables them to interlock, and walls built of them can be given steep slopes thereby effecting a saving in material, whilst their roughness is such that the swash height is less than for a smooth wall of the same slope. As far as the authors are aware their use has been mainly confined to harbour works, but on lengths of coast where amenity aspects, access for the public and the likelihood of children crawling into the interior of the wall do not need to be considered, there would seem to be scope under some conditions (for example, cliff protection) for the design of sea walls incorporating these blocks which are superior to rectangular blocks laid pell-mell. *Figure 15* shows tetrapods weighing about 4 Mg each used in strengthening the Marine Drive sea wall, Bombay. Where required much bigger units may be employed, those used to protect a jetty at Pointe Pescade, Algiers, Algeria, weighing about 40 Mg each.

Another form of permeable longitudinal sea defence (designed by Mobbs and English) is shown in *Figure 16*. It comprises a timber cribwork filled with concrete blocks and protects the coast at Christchurch. *Figure 17* shows another type of permeable revetment developed by Mr. Mobbs and constructed at Mundesley; built in conjunction with permeable groynes the build-up of foreshore was very rapid. The revetment is steel sheet piled at the base.

4.17 WAVE SCREENS

Figure 14 shows the wave screen on the Pett foreshore, Sussex, constructed between the years 1933 and 1936. Wave screens are another form of permeable longitudinal sea defence work and usually consist of timber piles driven well into the shingle with spaces between them about equal to their width. The tops of those at Pett are at the level of H.W.S.T. They are generally constructed in conjunction with other sea defence works; in the case of the one illustrated, in conjunction with a timber (box-type) barrier filled with shingle that is farther up the beach on the landward side of the screen and with a system of groynes. Their function is to reduce the energy of the waves.

For the system of sea defence described to be successful an adequate shingle feed is required. With the high costs of timber and labour and the relatively low cost of mechanical transport at the present time a wave screen of this kind would not generally be considered economical in England today, and the cheaper alternative would often be a system of groynes combined with artificial building up and replenishment of the beach (see section 2.6).

NOTE

The model tests described in this chapter were carried out, in the case of the Northern sea wall, by the Neyrpic Laboratories, Grenoble, and in the case of the Dymchurch sea wall, by the Hydraulics Research Station, Wallingford. The durability tests were conducted by Mr. J. Evans, B.Sc., C.Eng., F.I.C.E., Consulting Engineer.

BIBLIOGRAPHY

Design of Sea Defence Works in Relation to Height of Tide and Degree of Exposure, C. H. Dobbie, *Conference on North Sea Floods,* 1953; Instn. Civ. Engrs.

Sea Defences, C. H. Dobbie, Public Works Congress and Exhibition, 1952

Bitumen in Hydraulic Engineering, W. F. Van Asbeck; Shell Petroleum Co.

Use of Bitumen in Hydraulic Works, C. H. Dobbie and E. J. R. Kennerell, *J. Instn. Civ. Engrs.* vol. 33 (Feb. 1950)

Chapter 5

Examples of Sea, Estuary and Tidal River Walls

5.1 GENERAL

In the previous chapters all aspects of the design of sea and river walls have been discussed in detail. In this chapter therefore examples are given of actual walls of various types from simple river embankments to massive sea walls on exposed lengths of coast. The examples are illustrated by photographs and by simple line drawings indicating the layout, main dimensions of the walls and the levels of foreshore and of high tide. All these walls were designed on the basis of the principles outlined in the previous chapters and the reader seeking for an example of the application of any particular design principle will quickly find it in one of the walls illustrated. Because details of design have been discussed fully under previous headings no attempt has been made to describe the structural aspects of each wall at great length. For example, the line drawing may say baldly '380 mm × 380 mm × 200 mm interlocking concrete blocks'. These are described in detail in Chapter 4. The locations of the walls referred to are shown in *Figure 18*.

ESTUARY AND TIDAL RIVER WALLS

5.2 ESTUARY AND TIDAL RIVER WALLS

Since estuary walls are usually protected by the limited fetch in the estuary and by the saltings, the main need is to ensure that they are of adequate height, thickness and stability, and that sufficient protection is afforded against the small wave action caused by high winds or by navigation.

Earthwork heightening is limited by soil mechanics considerations and if the maximum practicable heightening by this means is insufficient, or if buildings prevent the addition of further clay for heightening, then the desired level has to be achieved by the construction of a concrete wall or similar structure.

5.3 TYPICAL TIDAL RIVER WALL PROTECTING A MAINLY INDUSTRIAL AREA

Figure 60 shows the river wall improvement at Erith where the desired level of 1 m above the tide level of 1 February 1953 has been achieved by heightening and strengthening with chalk and ash filling from local sources. The access provided along the top of the wall will be noted.

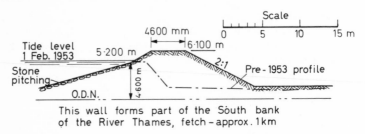

This wall forms part of the South bank
of the River Thames, fetch – approx. 1 km

Figure 60. Details of river wall at Erith

5.4 TYPICAL SHELTERED ESTUARY WALL PROTECTING A MAINLY AGRICULTURAL AREA

Figure 61 shows the wall heightening between Rushenden and Elmley constructed with clay taken from an adjoining delph ditch. The design includes provision of a landward berm for increased stability and for access.

5.5 TIDAL RIVER WALL HEIGHTENING AT RESTRICTED SITES IN INDUSTRIAL AREAS

Figures 62–66 illustrate typical methods of raising tidal river walls by the construction of reinforced concrete crest walls where buildings on the landward side or other structures prevent normal earthwork heightening.

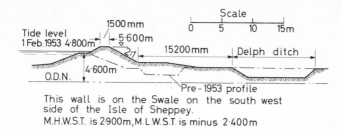

This wall is on the Swale on the south west side of the Isle of Sheppey.
M.H.W.S.T. is 2·900m, M.L.W.S.T. is minus 2·400m

Figure 61. Details of river wall between Rushenden and Elmley

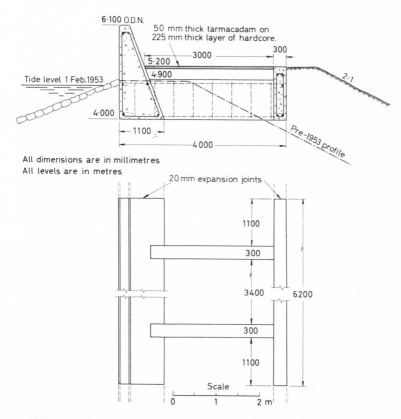

All dimensions are in millimetres
All levels are in metres

Figure 62. Details of crest wall at Erith on the south bank of the River Thames

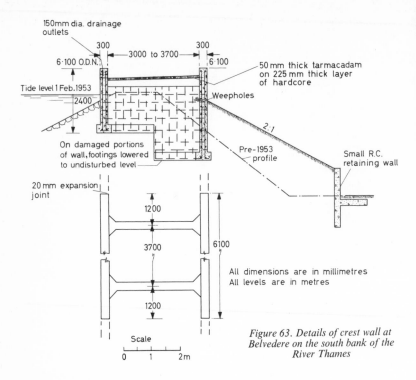

150mm dia. drainage outlets

6·100 O.D.N.

300

3000 to 3700

300

6·100

Tide level 1 Feb.1953

2400

On damaged portions of wall, footings lowered to undisturbed level

50 mm thick tarmacadam on 225 mm thick layer of hardcore

Weepholes

2:1

Pre-1953 profile

Small R.C. retaining wall

20 mm expansion joint

1200

3700

6100

1200

All dimensions are in millimetres
All levels are in metres

Scale

0   1   2m

Figure 63. Details of crest wall at Belvedere on the south bank of the River Thames

Figure 64. Crest wall at Erith

Figure 65. Crest wall at Belvedere

Figure 66. Crest wall at the Fuel Depot, Isle of Grain, under construction

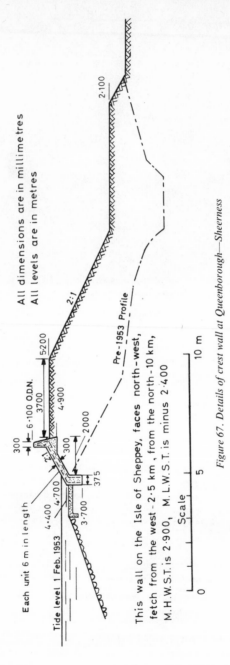

All dimensions are in millimetres
All levels are in metres

Each unit 6 m in length

Tide level 1 Feb. 1953

This wall on the Isle of Sheppey, faces north-west,
fetch from the west - 2·5 km , from the north - 10 km,
M.H.W.S.T. is 2·900, M.L.W.S.T. is minus 2·400

Pre-1953 Profile

Scale

0   5   10 m

Figure 67. Details of crest wall at Queenborough—Sheerness

Figure 68. Crest wall at Queenborough

5.6 EXPOSED ESTUARY WALL PROTECTING A BUILT-UP AREA

Figures 67 and *68* show the Queenborough wall at Sheerness. A top
level of +6·100 m. O.D.N. was required on this length. The safe
limit for the top of the earthwork, even with the provision of a berm,
was 5·200 m O.D.N. so that the remaining 0·9 m raising was achieved
by means of a reinforced concrete apron and wall which is designed
to resist safely the stresses that develop in it as settlement of the
newly placed clay takes place.

SEA WALLS FRONTED BY HIGH FORESHORES

5.7 SEA WALLS FRONTED BY HIGH FORESHORES

Sea walls of this type are those where storm waves break on the
foreshore before reaching the wall.

5.8 NORTHERN SEA WALL TYPE P

Figures 69 and *70* show a box-type of reinforced concrete (cellular)
crest wall employed in the heightening of those lengths of the Northern sea wall that are well protected by shingle on the foreshore.

*Figure 69. Northern sea wall cellular type P and Q reinforced
concrete wall under construction*
(By courtesy of Fox Studios Ltd.)

5.9 NORTHERN SEA WALL TYPE Q

Figures 19 and *71* show a wall similar to type P above but with the
addition of a seaward apron comprising a framework formed of the
reinforced concrete longitudinal toe wall and transverse walls, each
bay being faced with concrete blockwork. This type of wall was used
on lengths where there was less shingle giving protection than on the
P type lengths.

5.10 SEASALTER SEA WALL

Figures 47 and *48* show the wall at Seasalter. Here a wide foreshore
and shell and shingle deposits give good protection to the wall.

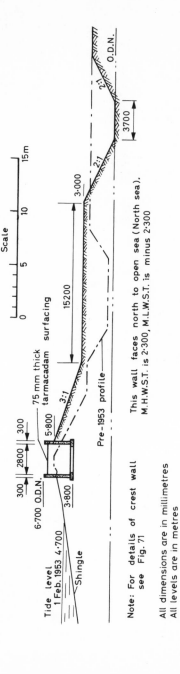

Figure 70. Details of Northern sea wall type P

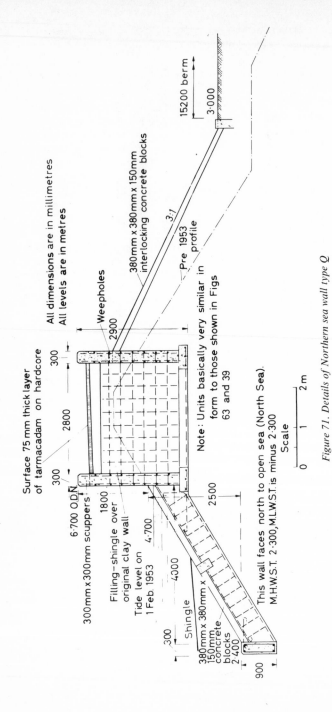

Figure 71. Details of Northern sea wall type Q

5.11 NAGDEN SEA WALL

Figures 72 and *73* give details of the Nagden wall. The seaward revetment consists of a framework of reinforced concrete walls with a wave wall at the crest, each bay so formed being filled with 200 mm interlocking concrete blocks. The connections between the upper and lower transverse walls are hinged (see Chapter 4) to allow for settlement of the newly placed clay on the landward side of the wall.

5.12 WALLAND SEA WALL

Figures 74 and *75* give details of the Walland sea wall, which is to the east of Rye. In many features this is similar in construction to, but larger than, the Nagden wall.

5.13 PETT SEA WALL

Figures 56 and *57* show the Pett wall, which is to the west of Rye. This is an example of the use of bitumen in sea defence works, and of a wide berm on the seaward revetment (see Chapter 4).

5.14 NORTHERN SEA WALL TYPE T

This wall, *Figures 76* and *78*, forms the crest unit of the main Northern sea wall design and has been constructed where there is more exposure than on type Q lengths but less exposure than on type U lengths.

5.15 NORTHERN SEA WALL TYPE U

This wall is as type T, but with additional seaward panels as shown in *Figure 77*.

SEA WALLS FRONTED BY LOW FORESHORES

5.16 SEA WALLS FRONTED BY LOW FORESHORES

Sea walls of this type are those where the depth of water in front of the wall at high tide is so great that storm waves break on the wall itself. *Figure 49* illustrates this condition.

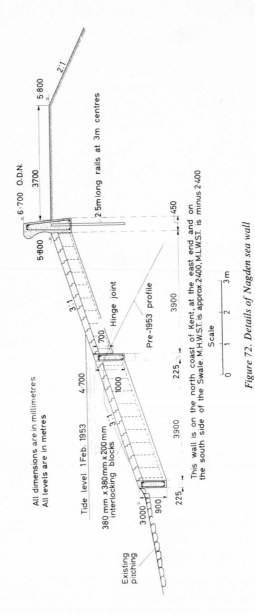

All dimensions are in millimetres
All levels are in metres

Tide level 1 Feb. 1953

380 mm x 380 mm x 200 mm
interlocking blocks

Existing
pitching

6·700 O.D.N.

2:1

5·800

5·800

3700

2·5 m long rails at 3 m centres

450

5·800

Hinge joint

Pre-1953 profile

3:1

700

4·700

3:1

1000

225

3900

3900

225

3000

900

225

This wall is on the north coast of Kent, at the east end and on
the south side of the Swale. M.H.W.S.T. is approx. 2·400, M.L.W.S.T. is minus 2·400

Scale

0   1   2   3 m

Figure 72. Details of Nagden sea wall

Figure 73. Nagden sea wall

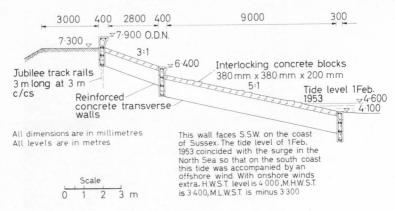

Jubilee track rails 3 m long at 3 m c/cs

Reinforced concrete transverse walls

Interlocking concrete blocks 380 mm x 380 mm x 200 mm

Tide level 1 Feb. 1953

All dimensions are in millimetres
All levels are in metres

This wall faces S.S.W. on the coast of Sussex. The tide level of 1 Feb. 1953 coincided with the surge in the North Sea so that on the south coast this tide was accompanied by an offshore wind. With onshore winds extra. H.W.S.T. level is 4 000, M.H.W.S.T. is 3 400, M.L.W.S.T. is minus 3 300

Scale
0   1   2   3 m

Figure 74. Details of Walland sea wall

Figure 75. Walland sea wall

All dimensions are in millimetres
All levels are in metres

380mm x 380mm concrete
blocks asphalt jointed

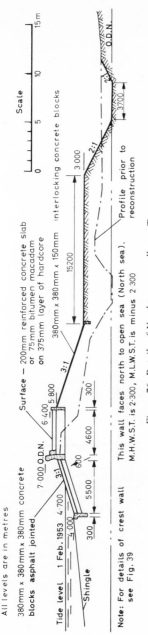

Note: For details of crest wall
see Fig. 39

This wall faces north to open sea (North sea).
M.H.W.S.T. is 2·300, M.L.W.S.T. is minus 2·300

Figure 76. Details of Northern sea wall type T

All dimensions are in millimetres
All levels are in metres

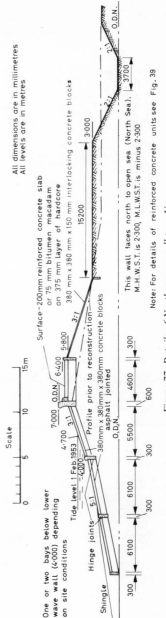

This wall faces north to open sea (North Sea).
M.H.W.S.T. is 2·300, M.L.W.S.T. is minus 2·300

Note: For details of reinforced concrete units see Fig. 39

Figure 77. Details of Northern sea wall type U

Figure 78. Northern sea wall type T under construction

5.17 DYMCHURCH SEA WALL

Figures 44–46 show details of this wall. The conditions it has to withstand are described in Chapter 4. It comprises a heavy stone blockwork facing, mainly of ragstone, laid on a clay wall.

5.18 NORTHERN SEA WALL TYPE V

Figures 39–43 show the main section of the Northern sea wall. The design of this wall is discussed in detail in Chapter 4. The lower panels are formed with timber and steel sheet piling because of the difficulty of placing *in situ* concrete at the lower levels and because settlement is not anticipated in the area of these panels.

Chapter 6

Closure of Breaches in Sea Walls

6.1 BREACHES

The most difficult breaches to deal with, in sea walls, are those in walls protecting low-lying land. Whilst breaches similar in all respects seldom occur, there are general principles of closure that apply to the successful closing of all breaches. Careful planning is of the highest importance—ill-considered expedients will seldom succeed.

A clear picture must first be formed of the site circumstances and details of the breach and of the labour, plant and materials available. Logical application of the basic principles of breach closure will then provide the correct solution to the problem. Breaches often happen in very inaccessible places and the construction of a suitable access then becomes a major part of the emergency works.

6.2 CAUSES OF BREACHES

The main causes of sea wall failure are set out in section 3.1. Breaches usually result from direct frontal erosion by wave action, flow through the fissured zone, scour of the landward face by over-topping, or combinations of these causes.

6.3 PRINCIPLES OF BREACH CLOSURE

The first aims must be to limit as far as possible further erosion of the breach and to reduce the volume and the velocity of the water flowing through it (see *Figures 79–82*).

A clear distinction must be made between (a) breaches through which the water flows only at high tide, and (b) those where the

Figure 79. Horsham Marsh Wall—breach at high tide

Figure 80. Horsham Marsh Wall—breach at low tide

Figure 81. Horsham Marsh Wall—ring wall in course of construction round breach (at high tide)

Figure 82. Horsham Marsh Wall—completed ring wall round breach

water flows continuously, either in or out according to the state of the tide.

In the case of (a) it is usual to fill the breach with clay-filled sand-bags (*Figure 83*). At a later date, when site conditions are suitable and plant, labour and materials are available, the bag-work can be removed and the wall can then be permanently reinstated. Sometimes it is possible to construct a ring wall of sand-bags, or of pickets and sheeting, or of trench sheeting backed by sand-bags, or

Figure 83. Closure of breach by clay-filled sand-bags at Motney Hill East Wall

of similar materials, on the seaward side of the breach to keep out the tide. This is the procedure usually adopted when it is expected that permanent reconstruction can be carried out fairly soon.

A condition intermediate between (a) and (b) can occur when, although water only enters the breach from the sea near the top of high tide, nevertheless because the marshes are fairly deeply flooded, water flows out through the breach as the tide drops. The ring wall should then be built on the marsh on the landward side of the breach.

In some cases it will be desirable to build ring walls both on the foreshore in front of the breach and on the marsh behind it. Efforts must also be made to get rid of the water on the marshes, as soon as possible, through existing gravity outfalls if they are of adequate capacity (see section 3.16) or through controlled breaches in the sea walls. Controlled breaches can be used when, as usually happens, the damage occurs at times of spring tides and the lower tides following do not reach the level of the water in the marshes.

Figure 84. Closure of Schelphoek breach. Ring wall on landward side of breach

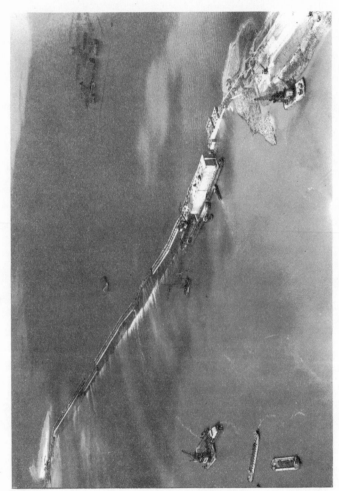

Figure 85. Schelphoek breach. One of the final openings in the ring wall being closed by a 'Phoenix' caisson

Breaches of type (b) present far greater difficulties. The first step is to stop the breach widening by providing, if needed, protection at the sides of the breach. The next step is to build a ring wall, usually on uneroded marshland on the landward side of the breach. Even while under construction this reduces the inflow and outflow of water which becomes less and less as the ring wall is built up until, when the top of the ring wall is above tide level (or the level of the water on the marshes, whichever is the highest), flow through the breach finally ceases. The Schelphoek breach in the Island of Schouwen, one of the biggest breaches ever to be closed, was closed by constructing a landward ring wall of caissons sunk on to a prepared bed of willow mattresses that prevented erosion under the caissons (*Figures 84, 85*). For large and difficult breaches of this kind it is customary to carry out model investigations to ensure the success of the operations.

6.4 BREACHES IN SEA WALL REVETMENTS

Breaches in sea wall revetments are generally less difficult to deal with than breaches that let water through.

Similar principles apply to emergency works for damaged facings as for wall breaches. Every effort must be made to prevent the damage spreading by providing protection at the perimeter of the damaged area. This is often in the form of concrete drop walls constructed with rapid-hardening cement or with a quick-setting additive to the cement. The bed of the damaged area is also covered with concrete of the same mix. Once repairs of this kind have been made, the permanent reinstatement works can be carried out when site conditions are more favourable and plant, labour and materials more readily available.

INDEX